DATE DUE			
JUN 0 6 1995			
MAY 3 1 1995			
OCT 1 5 1996			
OCT 1 1 1996			
APR 0 9 1999			
APR 0 9 1999			
3/20 found on shelf			

SAYNDAY'S PEOPLE

The Kiowa Indians and the Stories They Told

By

ALICE MARRIOTT

UNIVERSITY OF NEBRASKA PRESS · Lincoln

Winter-Telling Stories reprinted from the 1947 edition published by Thomas Y. Crowell, New York, by arrangement with the author. *Indians on Horseback* reproduced from the fourth printing of the 1948 edition published by Thomas Y. Crowell, New York, by arrangement with the author.

First Bison Book printing October, 1963

Most recent printing shown by first digit below:

.   3   4   5   6   7   8   9   10

Manufactured in the United States of America

FOREWORD TO THE BISON
BOOK EDITION

IN 1934, 1935, AND 1936, when the information that went into the two books that make up this volume was collected from the Kiowa Indians of southwestern Oklahoma, the life here described was gone. Only a few very old people had survived from the near margin of the North American Neolithic into the Air Age. Only they could tell, in tired voices, what it was like to live on the Great Plains before there were fences; when trees grew only along the watercourses, and when the buffalo grass was a dense carpet beneath their feet.

They remembered much, those old people. Tired as they were, they told their memories well. Sight as well as sound went into the telling. The movements of the sign language explained both daily living and deepest thought; the gestures always accompanied the relation of myths, until the time came when I could follow a story from motion alone. For the moments of oral storywriting, the old people rode again behind the buffalo or captured wild horses in the red sandhills. Once more, in telling of it, they tanned hides to make tipis, clothing, and moccasins;

containers and utensils were recreated in their words.

Weather permitting, we worked outdoors, where our eyes could rest on the shimmer of cottonwoods along the creek or be dazzled by the brown-gold ripple of summer coreopsis. When it rained we moved under the brush arbors Kiowas have always built for summer shelters, and if it was cold as well as rainy we went indoors. The tone of the storytelling changed then. Outdoors we spoke of big things, of people's beliefs and the ways they made their prayers; of why men painted pictures of people and animals, while women's art represented in geometric designs the inner life of the tipi.

Indoors, we spoke of details. The old men described how they made weapons and tools. They described the elaborate process of combing, brushing, braiding a man's hair, and how he finally painted his scalp. The old women told how to make brooms and rawhide cases. They described the way in which earth colors were mixed and used as paints. And they, too, discussed their cosmetic secrets and wondered aloud if they could ever learn the trick by which a white woman's skin remained so fair.

In those days we spoke through an interpreter, and the interpreter's job was the hardest of all. From one speaker to another she went, head turning and returning, as if she were watching a verbal tennis match. The speakers could rest during translation, but the interpreter never could. And if there had not been superlative interpreters there could have been no books.

Sometimes questions had to be asked to start the day's work moving. The first hour or two might be slow. Then the right word would trigger a quick response, and we were off. The stories and memories would tumble over one another and spill all over the notebook as the telling went on.

Portable tape recorders were a wistful dream; rural Indian homes seldom provided electricity. The only way of recording was with pencil and notebook. Each day's notes were conscientiously typed and filed before bedtime, while words and turns of phrase were still fresh in mind. Later they were compared with the published material available in libraries. During field seasons though, it was snatch and grab; seize and hold every bit of information the old people bestowed.

All through two summers I listened and watched as the elders talked: Spear Woman, the first wife of Hunting Horse, her foster son, George Hunt; Doc Frank Givvens; Old Man Tsoodle; Kiowa George Poolaw, and Sanko, whose only name means Prickly Pear. Their stories passed from Kiowa to English through two gifted sisters, the daughters of George Hunt, Ioleta MacElhaney and Margaret Tsoodle. I cannot thank them. I cannot thank any of my Kiowa friends. There are never thanks enough.

From this and later field work developed a way of thinking about my science. Anthropology, the study of man, has one enduring value. It is revealing man to himself through himself. Not the differences, but the similarities, among peoples are important. The qualities human beings have in common are greater than the traits they do not share. The pattern of human life from birth, through adolescence, adulthood, and senescence, to death, is the same everywhere.

One aspect of the living design may be emphasized at the expense of another; the Kiowa culture places the same emphasis and importance on old age that we accord to youth, for example. Such shadings intensify apparent differences, but they are only differences in degree, not in kind. The skill with which an anthropologist learns to increase and use his knowledge of human similarities determines the degree of his ability to reach understanding and rapport with people of other cultures.

Perception of similarities can be taught to and learned by all of us. The earlier in life the lesson comes, the better. School children perceive likenesses even more quickly than adults, if they are once taught that likenesses exist. For that reason, these two books were planned and written for younger readers.

Indians on Horseback was first written to an-
swer questions. Who are the American Indians?
Where did they come from? How did they live?
How did they name their children, make their
clothes, construct their shelters, cook their food?
Any anthropolgist is used to answering these
questions. Writing the answers in simple form,
for quick reference to questions about one area,
produced a book. It must have provided answers
for many readers, for teachers and school children have found it useful, and have said so.

Winter-Telling Stories was written before *Indians on Horseback*. The stories in that book are
ages old; the roots of some of them undoubtedly
lie in the Asiatic country-of-origin of all American Indians. But the stories are new, too; new
traits were added to the stories as they were added
to American Indian life. The same Saynday who
brought the buffalo from underground to feed
his starving people in the time of the beginnings,
ordered his clothes and his horse trappings from
a mail order catalog in later days.

Saynday is everywhere and he is every one of
us. We all have a desire to upset the balance of
the world; to change things for bad or good just
to see if we can do it. We are all vain; we are all,
sometimes, foolish. And we all want to do good,
and to be remembered after we leave this earth
because of the good we did. Trickster-Hero, Saynday's nearest parallel in Euro-American folklore

is Til Eulenspiegel or Merlin—and certainly no Euro-American ever thought of rolling them into one.

Stories which are the same as Saynday stories are told about other Trickster-Heroes. Each tribe gives the character its own name. Saynday is the same personality as Old Man Coyote of the Southwest, Komokoms of the Great Basin, or Gitchi-Manito of the Great Lakes. Still, to the Kiowas of the Southern Plains he is Saynday; Old Uncle Saynday, who is always coming along. His name is used today to scold bad children, "Daw! Sa, daym!" they are told, meaning "Messy! Like Saynday!"

How many Saynday stories there were in the buffalo world, I would hesitate to guess. There must have been hundreds; there may have been thousands. Oral literature is fluid. Some Saynday stories, still told, are outright pornography. But there is also a grim tale in which Saynday meets Smallpox, "dressed like a white man, in a tall hat and gloves," and buys freedom for the Kiowas from the great epidemic of the 1870's by sending the spirit of the disease on, away, to settle with another tribe, while at the same time contracting it himself.

One of the saddest things about this great short story collection of the Plains is that no one ever knew all of it, so we will never know all that went into it. Some of the stories now are fragments, scraps of great, lost epics.

From the time of their first writing, *Indians on Horseback* and *Winter-Telling Stories* "went together." They were concerned with the same people, in both time and space. *Indians on Horseback* is purposely broader in scope, with reference to tribes other than the Kiowa, than *Winter-Telling Stories*. Most of the information *Indians on Horseback* contains, however, was collected firsthand, from the Kiowa informants I have already named, and from Mrs. Mary Inkanish, a southern Cheyenne.

Far away and long ago, as well as here and now, the Plains Indians have always been people to appeal to the imagination. Say "Indian" to the average white American, and certainly to the average European, and the picture you conjure is that of wild, red-painted warriors, mounted on frantic, flashing horses; men and mounts alike barbarically gorgeous with feathers and the colors of quills, beads, painted buckskin, crimson trade cloth, and the dull sheen of German silver.

There was another side of Plains Indian life that was less frequently told. This was the women's side; the side of the persons who got the warriors ready for their expeditions. Statistically, females form fifty-two percent of our own population group. They probably comprised a higher percentage in most Plains Indian tribes, for we know that polygamy was an economic necessity to them. The surplus women in a fighting, hunting population must be cared for.

The earliest research on the Plains tribes was done by men anthropologists. Naturally, they worked largely with men. The culture portrayed in their writings was that of a man's world, and the picture of the fighting, buffalo-hunting lords of the earth that resulted was inevitable.

As the old men remembered their young lives, and told them to young men of another culture, they inevitably made good stories better. In the telling, they had been the patriarchal heads of their families; women had been their willing slaves.

It did not take me, as a woman anthropologist working with Kiowa women, very long to realize that this picture was not entirely accurate. The Kiowa woman, or indeed the woman of any other Plains tribe, was a strong personality in her own right. A weak woman could not have lived with men as strong as those of the Plains, at any time. The Plains Indian woman exercised absolute control within her home, and a considerable amount outside it.

Of course a Kiowa or Cheyenne lady did not push herself forward, raise her voice, or make a scene, any more than did her Victorian contemporary and counterpart. A wise Kiowa woman got her way and kept her household together as a wise woman does anywhere, by not asserting herself until such action was made necessary by circumstances. But she got her way, and held her household together into her own old age, nevertheless.

The children raised in this culture reflected behavior learned from each parent. Boys were left with their mothers and sisters until they were ten or twelve years old. Then, directed by older youths, they began to herd the family horses; take them to pasture and water in the mornings, and return them to camp at night. Gradually, imperceptibly, the boys moved out of the tipi world into the men's. From herding they graduated to horsebreaking; then to buffalo hunting, and finally they were permitted to accompany raiding parties as horseholders and cooks. Like mediaeval pages and squires, they were learning a man's responsibilities and attitudes by acting-out.

In the same way, girls drew back into the tipi world. They no longer fished in mud holes for crayfish, or twisted sticks into prairie dogs' fur to draw the rodents out of their holes. Instead of carrying shawl-wrapped puppies on their backs, they slung small sisters or brothers between their shoulders. The first fumbling stitches with awl and sinew, which had produced a girl's workbag and needle case, were tightened and prefected until she was skilled enough to make moccasins.

The same virtues were held up before both boys and girls. Speak quietly. Don't hurry. Wake early, so the sun will not see a lazy child. Remember to say your prayers and wash your face night and morning. Always be respectful to the old people, and go out of your way to help them, for they are your memory and your conscience.

Ideal behavior was not the same as real behavior, naturally. But the ideals existed plainly, for anyone to emulate. Even today, Kiowa parents hush their children when older people are speaking, and expect them to do a share of housework and work around the home.

Plains Indian women were the day-to-day craftsworkers of their people. A Kiowa woman made her home (and owned it); she was dressmaker, tailor, carpenter, cobbler, grocer, and cook for her family. She worked steadily and with pride in her achievements, day after day, year after year.

Men's work was sporadic. Men had highly-specialized skills: Weapon- and tool-making, naturalistic painting, and the manufacture of ceremonial objects. Some of their jobs were done once in a lifetime, and never repeated.

Hunting too was a part-time occupation. A family could use only so many buffalo in a year, and could prepare, store, and carry the meat from about four at a time. Surplus was disposed of by gifts to the less fortunate members of the group. Even so, there was a rest period between hunts, as there was between battles.

But from these simple facts two stereotypes were born, and they are with us today: "the lazy good-for-nothing buck Indian, lying around all the time," and "the slavelike squaw." They were and are about as true to life as stereotypes ever are.

However, once you have a stereotype, it is a hard thing to get rid of.

This combined book, then, is an attempt to show Plains Indian life as it was; the skills and thought; prayer and faith; fun and games and stories and songs that went into it equally with hunting and warfare. It is a book that tries to show the balance of Plains Indian life.

The American Indian culture of the Great Plains Area lasted only briefly in time. Its origin, as horses spread northward from New Spain, was in the early 1700's. It lasted almost precisely to the year 1872. Into that century-and-a-fraction was crammed all the excitement, color, passion, and drama that we associate today with life on the Plains. The horses opened the doors of the earth lodges, and brought the people out into the open sunlight of the mid-continent's land ocean.

To see this wave of change with understanding, we must think of the people who rode its crest. We must see that no matter what went on around them, they were still people, with the hopes and fears, successes and failures, that individuals have always known.

Saynday's People is their story. This is the way his people lived and worked, suffered and rejoiced. These are the stories they told about him, that old Uncle Saynday, who was always coming along . . .

CONTENTS

Winter-Telling Stories

For
the grandchildren of

GEORGE HUNT

who told these stories to them
and to me

WHAT SAYNDAY IS AND WHAT HE DID

THESE ARE STORIES that the Kiowa Indian people believe and tell about how things got started and came to be. Saynday was the one, they say, who got lots of things in our world started and going. Some of them were good, and some of them were bad, but all of them were things that make the world the way it is.

Saynday is gone now. He lived a long time ago, and all these things happened a long way back. When he was here on the earth, he was a funny-looking man. He was tall and thin, and he had a little thin mustache that drooped down over his mouth. The muscles of his arms and legs bulged out big and then pulled in tight, as if somebody had tied strings around them. He had a funny, high, whiny voice, and he talked his own language. His language was enough like other people's so they could understand it, but it was his own way of talking, too.

Because Saynday got things started in the world, he could make rules for the way they would keep on going. He could even make rules

1

for the way these stories were going to be told. These are the rules that Saynday made, and if you didn't keep them he could cut off your nose:

Always tell my stories in the winter, when the outdoors work is finished.

Always tell my stories at night, when the day's work is finished.

Always begin my stories the same way. They must always begin: SAYNDAY WAS COMING ALONG.

. . .

HOW SAYNDAY GOT THE SUN

SAYNDAY WAS COMING ALONG, and all the world was black. There was no sun on this side of the world, and the people were in darkness. The sun belonged to the people on the other side, and they kept it close by, so that no one could get it away from them.

As Saynday was coming along, he met some of the animals. There were Fox and Deer and Magpie. They were all sitting together by a prairie dog hole, talking things over.

"What's the matter?" said Saynday.

"We don't like this world," said Fox.

"What's wrong with this world?" said Saynday.

"We don't like the darkness," said Deer.

"What's wrong with the darkness?" said Saynday.

"It won't let things live and be happy," said Magpie.

"I guess we'd better do something about it," said Saynday.

So the four of them sat by the prairie dog hole, and they thought and they thought and they

3

thought and they thought. They were so quiet that the prairie dog stuck his head out of the ground, and when he saw them sitting there, he stayed still and joined in the thinking.

"There is a sun," said Saynday at last.

"Where is it?" said Fox.

"It's on the other side of the world," said Saynday.

"What's it doing there?" said Deer.

"The people who have it won't let it go," said Saynday.

"What good is it to us, then?" said Magpie.

"Not any," said Saynday. "I guess we'd better do something about it," said Saynday.

So they sat and they sat and they thought and they thought. They none of them moved at all.

Then Saynday said, "We could go and borrow that sun."

"It wouldn't really be stealing," said Fox.

"We don't want to keep it for always," said Saynday.

"We'd give it back to them sometimes," said Deer.

"Then things could live and grow on their side of the world," said Magpie.

"But they'd live and grow on this side, too," said Saynday.

Then Saynday got busy, because he'd finished his thinking. He could begin to do things now.

"How far can you run?" he said to Fox.

"A long long way," said Fox.

"How far can you run?" he said to Deer.

"A short long way," said Deer.

"How far can you run?" he said to Magpie.

"A long short way," said Magpie.

"I can't run very far myself," said Saynday, "so I guess I'll have to take it last."

Then he lined them all out and told them what to do. Fox was to go to the village on the other side of the earth, and to make friends with the people who lived there. That was the first thing to do, and that was the hardest. So Fox got ready and started out.

Fox traveled a long way, feeling his way along in the darkness. Then there was a little rim of light on the rim of the world ahead of him, like the sun coming up in the wintertime. He traveled toward the rim of light, and it got stronger and stronger till it was a whole blaze of light and filled all the sky ahead of him. Then he was up on a hill, and down below him was the village of the people who had the sun. Fox sat down on the hilltop and watched them while he made up his mind what to do.

The people were playing a game with the sun. They were lined up on two sides, and each side had four spears. They would roll the sun along the ground like a ball, and take turns throwing the spears at it. The side that hit it the most times won. One side was way ahead, and the other side was losing badly.

Fox went down the hill into the village and lay on the ground with his nose on his paws, and watched. They rolled the sun again, and the side that was ahead won two more points, and the side that was behind lost again.

So Fox said quietly, so just the captain on the losing side could hear him, "Good luck to the losers."

Nobody paid any attention, except the captain, and he just turned his head for a minute. Then they rolled the sun again, and this time the losing side won.

The captain came over and said to Fox, "Thank you for wishing us well."

"Good luck to your winning," said Fox, and this time that side won again.

Then they had some excitement. The side that had been winning before wanted to send Fox away, but the side that had been losing wanted to keep him. They argued and argued, but Fox's side was the strongest, and in the end he stayed.

Fox stayed and stayed and stayed and stayed in that village. He stayed till he knew it as well as he did his own home. He stayed till he knew the names of all the people, and what they all did and where they all lived. He stayed till he knew where they kept the sun all the time, and who were the men who watched it. He stayed till he knew all the rules of the game they played with the sun, and even till they let him play himself. All the time he was staying and playing, he was making his plan.

One day they had a big game. It was to decide the champions for that year. Fox was playing on the side that he had wished luck to in the beginning. Everybody else rolled the sun first because they had all been playing first, before he came. Then it was Fox's turn to roll. He took the sun in his paws the way they had taught him, and bent over as if he were going to send it along the ground. But instead of rolling it, he got a good start on his running, and he carried the sun along with him.

For just the first minute the people were so surprised to see their sun going away that they didn't know what to do. Then they were mad, and they started to run after Fox. But Fox was a fast runner and he could run a long way. That was why Saynday put him first. He ran and he ran, and at last he caught up with Deer.

Deer didn't even take time to look at the sun. He grabbed it away from Fox and started running with it himself. He ran and he ran, and just when he started to give out, he caught up with Magpie.

The sun village people were so far behind they couldn't be seen now, but Magpie didn't take any chances. He started right out with that sun, going as fast and as far away from there as he could. Just when his breath was gone, he came up to Saynday and handed the sun to him.

The sun village people were so far behind now that Saynday didn't bother to run. He just walked along with the sun over his shoulder like a big sack of meat. He walked along so easy that the others caught up with him. When they were back by their old prairie dog hole, they all sat down to rest.

"Well, now we have the sun," said Saynday.

"Now we can have light," said Fox.

"Now we can see what we are doing and where we are going," said Saynday.

"Now we can travel around," said Deer.

"Now plants will come up out of the ground and grow," said Saynday.

"Now there will be trees to live in," said Magpie.

"I guess we brought light to our world," said Saynday.

But the trouble was, there was too much light. It had been dark all the time and now it was light all the time. People could travel around all right, but they got tired out because it was light and they were traveling all the time. The plants and the trees could grow, but they never stopped growing. Magpie and his wife went to bed in a tree ten feet off the ground and waked up twenty feet up in the air. It was all very bothersome.

Finally the three friends went back to see Saynday.

Saynday was sitting on the ground in front of his tepee, admiring the sun shining on the ground in front of him.

"What's the matter?" he said.

"There's too much light," said Fox.

"We don't want so much," said Deer.

"We don't need so much," said Magpie.

"What can we do?" said Saynday.

"Try putting the sun somewhere else," said Fox.

"That's a good idea," said Saynday.

He put the sun in the tepee, but it kept on shining right through the walls.

"Put it up off the ground," said Deer.

"All right," said Saynday, and he balanced it on top of the tepee.

Whoosh! It burned the tepee right down.

"Throw it away," said Magpie.

"All right," said Saynday, "I don't want the old thing."

And he threw it straight up into the sky, and there it stayed.

"That's a good place for it," said Fox.

"It's far enough away not to burn things," said Saynday.

"It has plenty of room to move around," said Deer.

"It can travel from one side of the sky to the other," said Saynday.

"Now things can grow a little at a time," said Magpie.

"Now all the people on both sides of the world can divide the light evenly," said Saynday.

And that's the way it was, and that's the way it is, to this good day.

HOW SAYNDAY BROUGHT THE BUFFALO

SAYNDAY WAS COMING ALONG, and as he came he saw the animals dancing. They had built a shade out of brush, and the young men were dancing and singing.

"Well," said Saynday, "what's this?"

"This is a new dance," said Dragonfly. "We made it in honor of the sun you gave us. We call it the sun dance."

"It's a pretty dance," said Saynday. "Is everybody enjoying it?"

"Pretty much," said Owl. "There's one thing wrong, though."

"What's that?" said Saynday.

"We haven't any food," said Coyote. "Our young men are hungry."

"That's too bad," said Saynday.

"If they don't get something to eat pretty soon," said Fox, "they'll have to stop singing because they'll be too weak to go on."

"That certainly is too bad," said Saynday.

They all stood together and watched the dancing for a while. There was one bird man watch-

12

ing, too. Saynday noticed him specially. He looked like the crows that we have now, except that his feathers were white. That's the way the crows were to begin with. They all had white feathers.

This White Crow had a big quiver case in his arms, filled with a good strong bow and a lot of painted feathers. It was a fine set, all right, and he was taking good care of it. He stood and held it as carefully as if it were a baby.

"He certainly prizes that quiver case," said Saynday.

"He never puts it down," said Dragonfly.

"It's a good set, all right," said Saynday.

"He takes good care of it," said Owl.

"He looks as if he got enough to eat," said Saynday.

"He's fat and slick-looking, all right," said Coyote.

"I wonder where he gets it," said Saynday.

"Nobody knows for sure," said Fox.

"There ought to be some way to find out," said Saynday.

"We ought to get that quiver away from him," said Dragonfly.

They all stood and watched the dancing and thought and thought and thought and thought.

Then Saynday said, "How good are your eyes?"

"Pretty good," said Fox.

"Better than that," said Coyote.

"Real good," said Owl.

"Extra good," said Dragonfly.

"All right," said Saynday. "I know what we'll do. First we'll get him to let that quiver go. Then all of you must crowd up around him close, so I can look and see into it. Then when he goes away, we'll watch what he does. Each one can watch as far as he can see, and then the next one can start watching. That way we'll find out where he's living."

"All right," said his four friends, and they all went together over to where White Crow was.

"Hello," said Saynday.

"Hello," said White Crow.

"That's a fine quiver you've got there," said Saynday.

"I think it is," said White Crow.

"It looks pretty heavy," said Saynday.

"It *is* pretty heavy," said White Crow.

"Don't you get tired holding it?" said Saynday.

"Oh, I'm used to it," said White Crow.

But Saynday wouldn't give up. He'd set out to get that quiver, and he was going to have it.

"Everybody else is getting tired," he said. "They're all getting tired just from singing and drumming for the dancing. They're getting tired without holding anything. I should think you'd be tireder than anybody, holding that heavy thing in your arms that way."

But White Crow just laughed. "I don't get tired," he said.

Saynday put his head on one side, and looked at White Crow all over.

"I guess you don't," he said. "You don't look tired. You look as if you could hold that quiver case all day and sing all night, and never get tired at all."

"Oh," White Crow said, "I couldn't sing. I haven't any voice."

Saynday knew that this was true, but he had his mind made up what he was going to do.

"Oh," he said, "I think you have a good voice. It isn't like everybody else's voice. It's different. But I think it's a good voice in its own way."

White Crow laughed, kind of pleased. "Oh,"

he said, "you're just trying to make me feel good."

"No, I'm not," said Saynday. "I think you have a fine voice. And I've been watching you. You stand there tapping your foot right in time with the music. You never miss a beat. Anybody who can do that is a good drummer. Why, I bet you could go in there and start drumming and singing and take the place of all four men who are in there now. That's how good I think you are."

Then the four friends came crowding up close around Saynday and White Crow, and they began to flatter White Crow, too. They all told him over and over how good he was and how tired the singers were, and how he ought to go in and help.

Finally he said, "Well, all right. Just for a little time."

"I suppose you want somebody to hold your quiver," said Saynday.

"Well, yes, I suppose it would be better," said White Crow.

"Oh, you can just put it down on the ground," said Saynday. "Nobody will bother it."

"Well, I don't know," said White Crow. "Here, you take it. Hold it safe for me."

"Oh," said Saynday, "I don't want to hold that old heavy thing."

But he took it, and White Crow took the drumstick, and the four friends crowded up close while Saynday worked back to the edge of the crowd with the quiver in his arms. When he was back where no one was noticing, he opened the quiver case.

First he took out the bow, and then he took out the arrows, and he laid them all on the ground. Then he put his hand down deep, and found something and pulled it out, but it was just an extra bowstring, so he laid it down with the other things. Then he reached down, deep and deep to the very bottom, and there he found what he was looking for. It felt funny in his hand, and he pulled it out where he could see it. It was a chunk of buffalo meat and fat.

"Well," said Saynday, "this looks good to eat."

He put it in his mouth and chewed it. Then he knew that this was White Crow's secret. He did not know exactly what it was, but he did know that he was eating the best thing in all the world for Indians. He hid the rest of the piece in the quiver, and put back the extra bowstring, and the arrows, and the bow, and was sitting holding the quiver case in his arms when White Crow finished singing and came to get it.

"Goodbye," said Saynday to White Crow.

White Crow said, "Goodbye," and flew away from there, straight up into the air.

The four friends lay on their backs and watched him go. First Fox watched till his eyes gave out; the Coyote; then Owl. Just as Owl gave up and Dragonfly took over, they saw White Crow turn in the air and come flying back toward them. He came back till he was almost over their heads and they could all see him, and then they saw him dive down behind a little hill, and they knew that he lived right next door.

Saynday sat down to think some more.

When he knew what he would do, he said to his four friends, "Go and call the people together. Tell them to stop dancing and to break camp. Tell them to move on over the hill, and to leave me here behind."

So that was what the four friends did. They gave everybody Saynday's message, and everybody carried it out. They stopped dancing, and they moved. They left Saynday behind, with all the odds and ends and scraps that are always left behind on moving day. Then Saynday turned himself into a little white curly puppy, and sat down in the rubbish to see what would happen.

What happened was White Crow's little daughter. She came over to see if the people who moved had left anything behind that she could play with. While she was poking around in the odds and ends, she found the little puppy. She called and she whistled, but he wouldn't come to her. She ran after him and snapped her fingers, but he just ran away. Then she was sad and sat down and cried. The puppy came and sniffed at her ankles and jumped up in her lap and began licking her face. Then she caught him up in her arms and ran away home with him. She ran so fast and so hard that she ran right into her father.

"Look, father," she said. "Look what the people moved away and left behind."

White Crow looked and looked at the puppy, and the more he looked, the more he didn't like it.

"That doesn't look like any puppy I ever saw

before," he said. "Who ever heard of a puppy with a mustache?"

That was pretty bad for Saynday. There he was. He'd changed himself into a puppy, but he'd forgotten about his mustache, and there it stayed on his face. It was too late now, because they'd seen it. He couldn't change some more and take it off.

But White Crow's little daughter didn't care. She was spoiled and used to having her own way, and so she started to cry.

"I want to keep my little puppy," she said. "I don't want to throw him away."

Her father fussed around some more, but he couldn't stand seeing her cry, and so in the end he gave in.

"All right," he said. "You can keep your puppy, but you've got to be careful. Don't tell him any secrets, and don't show him where we get our meat."

That night they gave Saynday buffalo scraps for supper, and the food was so good and he ate such a lot of it that he went to sleep right away. He just dropped down under the little White Crow girl's bed, and he hardly noticed a big black rock that looked like a big black animal standing at the west end of the tepee.

In the morning they all waked up early. The White Crow mother got breakfast, and they all ate it.

Then the White Crow father said to the little girl, "Your mother and I have to go away for a while. We'll leave you here with your puppy. But just you remember what I said: Don't tell him any secrets and don't show him where we get our meat."

Then he and the mother flew up in the sky and away.

The little White Crow girl petted her puppy and played with him, till pretty soon she got tired. They went into the tepee to rest, and she saw the big black rock like a big black animal, standing there at the back.

"Come on," she said, "and I'll show you where we get our meat."

But Saynday was too good a puppy for that. He yawned and stretched out his back legs. Then he yawned again and stretched out his front legs. Then he flopped down on the ground with his tongue hanging out, and pretended to go to sleep.

"Don't do that," said the little White Crow girl. "Come on over here, and I'll show you."

But Saynday sat up and turned his back and pretended to scratch.

"You're a stupid puppy," said the little White Crow girl. "I'll make you look anyway."

And she picked him up in her arms, and carried him over to the rock. She put the puppy down and pushed back the rock, and there underneath it was a hole that went down under the earth. They leaned over and looked in, and there beneath them were all the buffaloes—the big bulls, and the middle-sized cows, and the little grunting calves. Then Saynday knew what kind of meat he had eaten, and he knew that this was the food that the Indian people should eat.

He got away from the little White Crow girl and jumped down into the hole, and began to chase the buffaloes out, jumping and barking to make them hurry up. The little girl got out of the way, and the buffaloes came rushing out from under the ground. There were so many of them and they came so fast that they made a noise like thunder with their hoofs.

White Crow was a long way away but he heard

it, and he and his wife came hurrying back as fast as they could fly, to catch whoever was turning all their buffaloes loose.

Sayday heard them coming, and he thought quickly. He turned himself into a cocklebur, and hid on the hind leg of the last of the buffalo bulls. They went tearing out of the hole past the whole White Crow family, and the next thing they knew they were outside in the sunshine, and the buffaloes were all around them. Sayday turned into himself again, and stood on the grass and faced the herd.

"This is the grass that you are to eat," he said, "and this is the country that you are to live in. Spread out from here, south and west and north and east, wherever this buffalo grass will grow, so the people who live in this country will find you and have food. Don't go up into the mountains on the west or into the thick timbers on the east, but spread out up and down in the middle where the flat plains are, and make food for all the people of the plains."

And the buffaloes heard him and obeyed, and that's the way it was, and that's the way it is, to this good day.

HOW THE WHITE CROW TURNED BLACK

SAYNDAY WAS COMING ALONG, and as he came he saw the buffalo herds that he had scattered out over his good plains. There were little family and big tribe bunches of buffaloes everywhere. Saynday got up on a high hill to the west, and looked out over them.

At first when he looked, he saw all the buffaloes grazing. Then they would throw up their heads and jump and run and scatter out. He was too far away to see what was making them do it, but he could see what they were doing. He got to wondering what was bothering his buffaloes.

He went down on the plains and walked along till he came to a village where some of his friends lived. There were Dragonfly and Deer and Magpie, and the old Spider Woman.

"Good morning, friends," said Saynday.

"Good morning," said his friends. "Sit down and stop walking."

So Saynday sat down. Old Spider Woman went and got him something to eat. All she brought him was wild potatoes, and that surprised Saynday.

"How does this happen?" he said. "Won't anybody go hunting to get meat for you?"

"Everybody goes hunting," said Spider Woman.

"Then where is the meat?" said Saynday.

"There isn't any meat," said Magpie.

"Where are my buffaloes?" said Saynday.

"Out on your plains," said Deer.

"Then why don't the hunters get them?" said Saynday.

"Somebody is scaring the buffaloes," said Dragonfly.

"That's pretty bad," said Saynday.

"It's bad, all right," said Spider Woman. "Every time the hunters get up close enough to kill a buffalo, *he* comes flying straight down out of the sky and scares the herd away."

"Who does that?" Saynday wanted to know.

"It's that White Crow," said Magpie.

"What does he want to do that for?" asked Saynday.

"He says the buffaloes were all his till you came along," said Deer.

"He was supposed to be keeping them for everybody," said Saynday.

"Well, but he says you stole them from him," said Dragonfly.

Saynday sat there and thought and shook his head. Then he shook his head and thought some more. His world seemed to go on making up new problems for him to do things about. He thought a long time till he thought up a plan.

"All right," he said, "I'll fix it so you have some buffalo meat."

"Will you fix it so we get rid of White Crow?" asked Spider Woman.

"I'll do the best I can," said Saynday. "Now this is my plan: I'm going to turn into a buffalo. Into the bones inside the buffalo. I'm going out there on the plains and you can come and shoot me. Get the hide off the meat and the meat off the bones, but don't cut into the bones themselves. If you do, you'll hurt me, and if you hurt me I'll yell."

So Saynday stood up and turned himself into a buffalo. Into the bones inside the buffalo. He went out on the plains all by himself, and settled down to graze like a buffalo. Pretty soon there was a speck in the sky, and White Crow came swooping down and lit on the grass in front of him.

"Look out," said White Crow.

"What's the matter?" said Buffalo-Saynday.

"The hunters are coming," said White Crow. "You'd better get ready to run. As old as you are and as tough as you are, they'll kill you and eat you."

"Oh," said Buffalo-Saynday, "I'm not afraid of just some old hunters."

"Well," said White Crow, "you certainly aren't like any other buffalo I've ever seen. Maybe you aren't a buffalo at all."

But Buffalo-Saynday just kept on eating the grass, and behind him he could hear his friends slipping up closer and closer, and getting ready to shoot.

White Crow was getting more and more excited.

"You'd better look out," he said. "They're getting closer and closer. They're getting their arrows out of their quivers. They're stringing their bows. They're taking aim ready to shoot. Look out! Whoosh! You're dead."

And Buffalo-Saynday fell over on the grass and was a dead buffalo.

White Crow went and hid behind a clump of grass. Deer and Magpie and Dragonfly came up with their knives and got ready to skin their buffalo. They took off the skin and then they took off all the meat. They knew that even if it was magic meat, the people were hungry enough to eat it. They even took their knives and cut off the thin slices of meat between the rib bones. They were slow and careful, so as not to cut any of the bones themselves. Then they loaded the meat into the skin and dragged it away for Spider Woman to cook for them.

All the time they were working, they knew that White Crow was hanging around. He didn't speak to them and they didn't speak to him. They even pretended to each other that he wasn't there. They just went on working as if he were nowhere near.

When Saynday's friends had gone, White Crow came out from behind the clump of grass and flew over to the buffalo bones.

"There!" he said. "You see what I told you? I said the hunters would come and kill you. You certainly didn't act like any buffalo I ever saw."

He jumped up and lit on the skull and pecked

at it, and the skull jumped just a little, because the pecking tickled.

"There!" said White Crow. "That's what I thought. I never heard of bones that went jumping around."

He jumped down and walked over to the big hip bone, and climbed up on it.

"I bet it's that Saynday fellow," he said to himself, and he pecked at the big hip bone. The pecking was sharp enough to hurt this time, but the big hip bone stayed still.

"It didn't have a mustache, though," said White Crow. "When he turns himself into things, they have mustaches. That's like that Saynday. He never does a good job. Just too lazy to care whether he finishes things up."

That made Saynday so mad that he could hardly lie still, but he waited and he waited. White Crow climbed out on the buffalo back bone and ran along it, and that tickled the way it tickles when someone runs a finger down the middle of your back. Saynday couldn't help shivering just a little.

"That's what I thought!" said White Crow. "These bones are alive!"

And he jumped on the ribs and began to peck and tickle as fast and as hard as he could. That was just what Saynday was waiting for, and he closed his rib bones together like the fingers of a hand, and caught White Crow in them good and tight. Then he turned into himself again, standing there holding White Crow in his hands.

"That's what you thought," he said. "When you start thinking, you ought to do something about it. Just thinking isn't going to do you any good."

And he carried White Crow in his hands back to camp.

All his friends were waiting for him there. They had the meat all cut up, and they had built a fire to smoke the meat and dry it out so it would keep a long time when they were traveling around.

"Here's the one that's making the trouble," said Saynday.

"What are we going to do with him?" asked Magpie.

"We ought to do something to punish him," said Deer.

"It ought to be something he'll always remember," said Dragonfly.

"Give him to me," said Spider Woman.

"This is a big job," said Saynd0ay.

"I can do it," said Spider Woman. "You give him to me."

So Sayndoay gave White Crow to Spider Woman, and she held him tight between her hands, and began to make motions with them, around him and over him. She made four motions up and four motions down, and four motions south and four motions west. She was spinning her web, but none of the others noticed it. Then she made four motions north and four motions east, and then she threw her arms out wide, and White Crow flew out from between them and up and up toward the sky.

"Now you see!" said Magpie.

"I knew what would happen," said Deer.

"You turned him loose," said Dragonfly.

"I told you it was too big a job for you to do," said Sayndoay.

But Spider Woman just held up her hand.

"Hush and be quiet," she told them, "I know what I'm doing."

And she began to pull toward her with her hands, as if she were pulling something in. That was what she was doing. She had fastened her web around White Crow's body, and now she pulled in on the web till she had him back in her hands again.

Then Spider Woman walked over to the fire where she was smoking the meat. She took the meat away from the fire, and tied White Crow where it had been. Then she got green wood and put it on the fire, so it made a big smoke. White Crow hung there and smoked and choked and choked and smoked till his feathers turned black. Then Spider Woman unfastened him and took him down.

"Now you can go," she said. "Your feathers will never be white again. You will always be black, to show that you tried to starve the people. You will never do your own hunting. You will have to hang around old bones that are lying out on the grass and eat what other people have left. You will never be proud any more. That is your punishment for what you have done."

And that's the way it was, and that's the way it is, to this good day.

WHY THE DEER HAVE SHORT TEETH

SAYNDAY WAS COMING ALONG, and as he came he saw that something had gone wrong again in his world. The deer were killing the people. When the deer were first made, they had long sharp hoofs so they could paw up the grass, and long sharp teeth so they could bite it off down to the roots. Then they found out that they could fight with those sharp hoofs and teeth, and hurt each other, and then they began to hurt other people. It was pretty bad.

Everywhere Saynday went, there was mourning and crying. All the people were grieving because the deer were killing them. The prairie dog and the gopher and the ground owl, and even the skunk, had all lost friends or relations, so they were all sitting around crying. They asked Saynday please to do something to save them from those fierce deer.

Most times when Saynday had thinking to do, he had friends around to help him with it, but this time they were all too unhappy to think. Saynday had to do all his thinking alone.

So he sat down on the banks of Cottonwood Creek, and he thought and he thought and he thought and he thought. He thought till he got too hot to go on thinking, and then he crawled into Cottonwood Creek with all his clothes on, and sat there up to his neck in the water, still thinking.

Where he sat down the water was clear and cool, and there was gravel and sand on the bottom, so it made a nice bathtub. But farther down the stream, the sand and gravel stopped, and there was a thick mud bottom. Saynday was thinking so hard about the deer that he forgot about the mud, and the stream carried him along and sat him down squash in the thick of it before he remembered. Then was when he had his idea.

He climbed up out of the mud of Cottonwood Creek and hunted along the banks till he found where there were some stones. There were big flat stones that you could make a walk of, and there were big round stones that you could make grindstones of. Saynday began picking up as many of them as he could carry, and bringing them back to where the mud was thick in the bottom of Cottonwood Creek.

First he made a big pile of the grindstone rocks on the other side. Then he began laying the paving stones across the flat creek bed, like a walk. It took him a long time, but at last he had everything ready. Then he got into the water and began to stir up the mud. First it came up to his ankles, but that wasn't enough. Then it came up to his knees, but that still wasn't enough. Then it was up over his waist, but that wasn't enough, either. And then it was up over his shoulders.

"There!" he said. "That ought to be enough. That'll be way over the deer's backs."

Then he climbed out of the muddy water and washed himself off, and went away looking for the fierce deer. When he found them, they were down in a little valley, pawing up the grass and turning it over with their sharp hoofs, and biting it off down to the roots with their sharp teeth. Saynday got up on a little hill where he could see them and they could see him, and he began to yell at them.

"Oh," he said, "what bad people! I didn't know there were such bad people in my whole world!"

The chief of the deer looked up and snapped

his teeth at Saynday.

"Go away," he said. "We aren't bothering you. Go away and stop bothering us."

He looked fierce.

Saynday jumped up and down and yelled louder than ever.

"Those are bad people," he yelled. "They are frightening everybody. They are killing everybody. Nobody likes them any more. They don't even like themselves."

The deer chief scowled at him.

"Go on away," he said. "I warn you, just go clear on away."

But Saynday wasn't going to go.

"Even the little children don't like them," he howled. "They're the worst people in the whole world."

Then the deer chief turned and ran at Saynday, and all the other deer ran, too. That was what Saynday was waiting for. He turned and ran down the hill toward Cottonwood Creek, and all the deer came tearing after him, just as hard as they could chase. Saynday ran into the water and along the stones to the other side, but the deer were running too hard to look where they were going, and they got stuck in the mud clear over their backs. That was what Saynday wanted.

When they were all stuck tight in the mud, he got his grindstone rocks, and waded out into the muddy water. He took the deer one at a time, and filed off their upper teeth right to the gums.

"Please don't do that," said the deer chief.

"Why shouldn't I?" asked Saynday.

"It hurts us too much," said the deer chief.

"You've been hurting other people," said Saynday.

"We'll all starve without any teeth," said the deer chief.

"You've been killing other people, haven't you?" said Saynday.

"We'll never do it again," said the deer chief. "Just leave us our lowers so we can eat, and we'll never hurt anybody any more."

"All right for now," said Saynday. "I'll leave you your lowers for now. But I want you to hear what I say. You are to go in the woods on the edge of the plains and hide there. When you want water to drink, you can come out to the creeks and the ponds, but then you'd better go back in the woods. Because you have hurt all the other people, any of them has the right to hurt you. You will have to watch out and hide and be timid, and you can never eat anything any more but grass and green leaves."

And the deer pulled themselves up out of the mud and went and hid in the woods, and that's the way it was, and that's the way it is, to this good day.

WHY THE ANT IS ALMOST CUT IN TWO

SAYNDAY WAS COMING ALONG, and as he came he saw little Red Ant with a big sack over her shoulder. Little Red Ant was different in those early days. Her head and her body were all in one piece, with no neck between them. When she carried her big round sack it looked like one ball carrying another and rolling along the ground.

"Hello, there," said Saynday. "You look as if you were hot."

"I am hot," said little Red Ant. "It's a hot day."

"Sit down and rest," said Saynday, "and let's talk things over."

"All right," said little Red Ant.

They sat down and rested in the shade of a prickly pear, and Saynday made himself small enough to talk comfortably to little Red Ant.

"I've been thinking a lot," said Saynday.

"What have you been thinking about?" asked little Red Ant.

"I've been thinking about death," said Saynday. "My world and my people have been going on quite a while now, and things are beginning to get old and die sometimes."

"What's wrong with that?" said little Red Ant. "It makes room for new people."

"The people who die don't like it," said Saynday.

"There isn't any way to make them stop dying," said little Red Ant.

"No, but there might be a way to bring them back," said Saynday. "I've been thinking and thinking and thinking about it, and I think I know a way to bring them back when they've been dead four days."

"Well, it sounds rather silly to me," said little Red Ant.

"I don't see anything silly about it," said Saynday.

"I think it is," said little Red Ant. "The way things are now, the people who die off are old. They've had a good time and lived life out. When they go, it doesn't hurt them. Then there is a place for a new person to come along and enjoy life. I think the new ones ought to have a turn."

"That's the way it is now," said Saynday, "but

maybe it won't always be that way. Maybe some of the young people will get killed off by accident. Then we ought to have some way to bring them back so they can enjoy their full lives."

"I don't think you need to," said little Red Ant. "If they're so stupid they go and get killed, it's just their own faults."

"All right," said Saynday. "I wanted to know what you thought. Now that I know, I will let there be death. When things and people die, they won't come back to this world any more. Now I have to go and see some more of my world. Goodbye."

And he and little Red Ant went their separate ways.

Four days later Saynday was coming back, and he came to that same prickly pear. There was mourning and crying all around. He looked down on the ground and saw little Red Ant. She was sitting in the shade of the prickly pear and crying as if her heart would break. Saynday made himself little again, and sat down beside her.

"What's the matter?" said Saynday.

"Oh, it's my son," said little Red Ant.

"What happened to your son?" said Saynday.

"A buffalo stepped on him," answered little Red Ant, "and now he's all gone dead."

"That's too bad," said Saynday.

"It's terrible," said little Red Ant.

And before Saynday could do anything, she pulled his knife out of his belt and cut herself almost in two, just above her shoulders. Saynday thought there had been enough dying already for one morning, so he took the knife away before she could cut herself clear in two.

"There," he said, "you see how it is. That's the way people feel when some one they love dies. They want to die too. If you'd let me have my way, your son would have come back at the end of four days. But you thought there would be too many people in the world if that happened. So now you know why I wanted to do that. For all the rest of the world, people will keep on dying. And for all the rest of the world, you will go around cut almost in two, to remind you of what you did to everybody."

And that's the way it was, and that's the way it is, to this good day.

This is the last of the Saynday-does-good stories, but there are some Saynday-makes-trouble stories, too. Follow and read along, and you'll see how Saynday could make things go wrong.

HOW SAYNDAY GOT CAUGHT IN A
BUFFALO SKULL

SAYNDAY WAS COMING ALONG, and as he came he saw a dried-up old buffalo skull lying on the ground. All the air around was filled with the sound of drumming. It was a small little drumming that seemed to come out of the ground at his feet. Saynday stopped and stood and studied over it.

"Well," he said to himself, "I wonder where that noise is coming from?"

He looked up in the sky and around to his left and around to his right, as far as he could see, and then he got down and knelt on the ground and looked along the earth. He looked into the buffalo skull, and there he saw where the noise was being made. The buffalo skull was full of field mice, and the mice were having a sun dance.

All the lady mice were back in a ring out of the way with their children. All the old men mice were over at one side with their big drum, beating on it and singing. All the young men mice were in the middle, dancing as hard as they could go, and keeping time with the drumming and the singing.

"Well, now," said Saynday, "this is something worth seeing!"

And he stretched out on the ground, and stretched out his neck along the ground, and he watched and he watched and he listened and he listened. The singing and the drumming and the dancing went on, and Saynday worked up closer and closer along the ground, without paying any attention to anything but the field mice and their sun dance.

The mice were dancing and drumming and singing so hard that they didn't notice Saynday either, and the first thing any of them knew he had stuck his head right through the door of the buffalo skull, and there he stuck.

Well, the mice were mad! One minute they were dancing away in a nice shady shelter, and the next minute their shelter was up in the air on somebody's shoulder, and was dancing around itself.

"Wow!" said Saynday. "Let me out! Get me out! I can't see anything! Where am I? What am

I doing? Why doesn't somebody tell me these things?"

But the field mice were all of them scared and mad, and they all of them ran away. They left Saynday hopping up and down, first on one foot and then on the other, right out in the middle of the bald-open prairie.

When he found that he couldn't get out and he couldn't see, Saynday began really to think about how he was going to get home. First he tried crawling along the ground, but that was too slow and bumpy. Then he stood up and tried to walk along the way he always had, but he kept stubbing his toes and falling down. Finally he decided that he'd just have to feel his way along.

So he walked along slowly, putting his arms out in front of him, and pretty soon he came to a tree. He could feel one of the twigs in his hand.

So he stopped and said, "Who are you?"

And the tree gave a little windy sigh, and said, "I'm mesquite."

So Saynday shook his head and said, "You grow on the high and windy plains, and you won't do. Am I headed right for Cottonwood Creek?"

And the mesquite tree sighed again and said, "Yes."

So Saynday went on, feeling his way and feeling his way, till he felt another twig in his hand.

Then he stopped and said, "Who are you?"

And the tree rustled and shivered all over its top branches, and said, "I'm wild plum."

And Saynday said, "Well, I'm going right, anyway, but you still won't do. Am I headed right for Cottonwood Creek?"

And the wild plum shivered and rustled and said, "Yes."

So Saynday went on, feeling his way and feeling his way, till he felt another twig in his hand.

Then he stopped and said, "Well, who are you?"

And the tree gave a solid creak and a groan, and said, "I'm elm."

And Saynday said, "Well, I'm almost there. Are you growing near the banks of Cottonwood Creek?"

And the elm tree creaked and groaned, and said, "Right up the bank and over the slope."

And Saynday hurried ahead. He had easy going now, because it was all downhill, and he could feel his way along down the slope. He kept going and going and feeling and feeling, till he felt a thin little switch of a twig in his hand.

He said, "Are you willow?"

And the little tree sobbed, and said, "I'm the weeping willow."

And then Saynday knew where he was. He crawled into Cottonwood Creek and let the current carry him down, over the sand and over the shallows, over the gravel and over the deep pools, and even through and over the slimy sticky mud, till he came to the place where his own camp was.

All the people in Saynday's camp were sitting and resting, because it was the end of the day and they had finished their work.

Fox looked out at Cottonwood Creek, and he said, "Well, I see something pretty funny out there."

Magpie looked, too, and he said, "That certainly is something strange."

Deer looked, and said, "I can't be sure just what it is."

And Dragonfly looked, and said, "It's a buffalo skull floating on the water."

Then they were all frightened, because who ever heard of a buffalo skull that floated? They wished that they had Saynday there to tell them what to do, but since he wasn't there, they thought they'd better do something themselves.

"Run and get your arrows," said Fox.

"And your bows," said Magpie.

"Get ready to shoot," said Deer.

"Everybody let go," said Dragonfly.

So they all shot fast and straight at the floating buffalo skull, and Saynday inside could hear the arrows rattling like hail on the outside of the skull. Then he was bothered. He knew he was home, because he knew the voices, but his own people were shooting at him. He stood up in the water and waved his arms.

"Don't shoot! Don't shoot!" he yelled, but the buffalo skull smothered the sound, and what came out was, "Mooon't mooooot! Mooon't moooooooot!"

"It speaks a foreign language," said Fox.

"I never heard anything like it," said Magpie.

"It certainly is funny-sounding," said Deer.

"But it sounds a little familiar, too," said Dragonfly.

"Maybe we'd better shoot again," said Fox.

"It's coming this way," said Deer.

"It looks familiar below the skull," said Magpie.

"It is familiar," said Dragonfly. "It's Saynday."

Then they all knew him, and they rolled on the grass laughing and laughing at the mess he'd got himself into.

"Don't do that," said Saynday. "Come here and get me out."

Then Deer, who was really very tenderhearted, said, "All right, we'll help you."

And he picked up a stick and started trying to pry the skull off Saynday's head.

"Don't do that," said Saynday. "That hurts."

"All right," said Fox. "We'll try something else."

And he took his stone hammer and whammed down hard on top of the skull, and the skull went all to pieces on the ground around Saynday.

"That hurts, too," said Saynday.

"Well, it got you out," said Fox. "That's what you wanted us to do. Now you let that be a lesson to you. You stay at home and mind your own business, and don't go around bothering other people again."

But that was the thing that Saynday couldn't do and wouldn't try.

HOW SAYNDAY RAN A FOOT RACE
WITH COYOTE

SAYNDAY WAS COMING ALONG, and as he came he saw a prairie dog town. The sun was way up in the middle of the sky, showing that it was noon and time to be hungry. Saynday was hungry, but the prairie dogs were all outside their holes, dancing in the hot sun as if they had never heard of mealtimes.

"Well," said Saynday to himself. "There's a fine fat lot of prairie dogs. Just what I've been wanting for my lunch."

But he hadn't any bow and he hadn't any arrows, and he hadn't any way to get the prairie dogs so he could have lunch.

Still, he walked on over to where the dance was going on, and said, "Hello, there."

The prairie dogs didn't pay any attention. They just went on and on, dancing and dancing. Saynday looked around and saw a big stick lying on the ground, and he reached out and got it.

"That's a funny kind of dancing," he said out loud.

This time when he spoke, the prairie dogs looked up and listened, but they didn't stop dancing.

"I know a better kind of dancing than that," Saynday said.

That made the prairie dogs stop, because they were vain about the way they danced.

"What kind of dancing do you know?" said a big fat old prairie dog.

"It's a different kind," said Saynday. "It's a kind some foreign tribes do."

"All right," said the big fat old prairie dog. "Suppose you show us how to do it."

"All right," said Saynday. "This is the way. Everybody has to make a line. Then you all join hands and close your eyes, and dance forward while I sing. There's a hard song that goes with this dance, and if I tried to teach it to anybody, it would take so long to learn that your children would have to do the dancing."

"Well," said the fat old prairie dog, "it won't do any harm to try that dance."

But one little prairie dog, way down at the end of the line, said to herself, "I don't like that kind of dancing."

All the rest of the prairie dogs liked it, though, and they all joined hands and shut their eyes, and began to dance forward in a long line. Saynday stood behind them with his big stick in his hand and pounded the stick on the ground for a drum. He sang:

"Prairie dogs, prairie dogs, wag your tails.
Now is the time to dance the best—
Now is the time to dance the best—
Huh! Huh! Huh! Huh!"

And every time he said "Now" or "Huh!" he hit one of the prairie dogs on the head and killed it. Just when he got to the end of the line, the little prairie dog who didn't like that kind of dancing opened her eyes and saw what was happening. Quick as a flash, quicker than Saynday could hit, she ran into her hole and hid.

"Oh, well," said Saynday, "let her go. It would be pretty bad for people if I killed off all the prairie dogs."

Then he started gathering up the meat for his lunch, and getting things ready for cooking. He found an old iron kettle some people had left behind when they broke up camp, and he filled it full of water. Then he gathered up sticks and chips and odds and ends, and built a fire with them. Then he put the kettle on the fire, and sat down to wait while his soup cooked.

While he was sitting there, sniffing the good smells that came from his cooking, Coyote came along. He smelled the cooking smells, and he looked over the edge of a little rise, to see where they were coming from. He saw the kettle boiling on the fire, and Saynday sitting there smelling the soup and feeling pleased with himself because getting his lunch was so easy. Coyote sat down on the other side of the rise to do some thinking.

"I'm going to get that lunch away from Saynday," he said to himself. "I don't know how he got it, but I know he played a trick on somebody. He wouldn't look that pleased if he hadn't."

Then Coyote thought of a plan.

He went away a little way, and gathered sunflower sap and milkweed down, and stuck them together all over his body so he looked as if he were covered with sores. Then he found a tall crooked stick, and leaned on it as if it were a cane. He went limping over to where Saynday was sitting and smelling his soup and feeling pleased with himself.

"Hello, friend," he said.

And Saynday said, "What are you doing around here?"

"I thought I smelled your good soup cooking, friend," said Coyote.

"It's my soup," said Saynday in a hurry, because he was greedy and didn't want to divide.

"I'm very hungry," said Coyote.

"So am I," said Saynday.

"Please give me a little of your soup," said Coyote.

"No," said Saynday. "I just barely have enough for myself now. I haven't any to give away."

"You see the shape I'm in," said Coyote. "All bent and crippled with rheumatism, and covered with sores. I'm in no condition to go hunting for myself. Of course, as soon as I get better, I will go hunting, and then I'll gladly share anything I get with my neighbors."

"No," said Saynday, and he took the soup kettle off the fire and set it on the ground to cool.

"Well," said Coyote, "I'll tell you what. If you

won't give me any of your soup, will you gamble with me for it?"

"I don't know what you mean," said Saynday, stirring the soup to make it cool faster.

"Well," said Coyote, "it's a long way over there to Mt. Scott. It's just about long enough for the soup to cool while a fast man runs over there and back. So while you're waiting for the soup to cool, why don't you race me over to Mt. Scott and back? The winner gets the pot of soup."

Saynday looked at that poor, bent-over old Coyote, and he just laughed and laughed.

"That's a fine idea," he said. "You must want the soup pretty badly. The way you are, you couldn't run ten feet."

"Well," said Coyote, "I'm willing to try if you are."

Saynday felt pretty safe about his pot of soup by this time, so he said, "Oh, I'll race you for it, if you like. I'll even tie rocks on my arms and legs to make the race fair."

And that was what he did. He loaded himself down with rocks, and every time he stopped tying them on, Coyote would give a kind of a gasp, and say, "It isn't really a race, a fine healthy man like you against a wreck like me." He was just laying it on.

At last they were ready, and Saynday drew a line on the ground for a starting place. They stood up to it side by side.

Then Coyote said, "Go!"

Coyote started hobbling along, bent over his cane, and just about even with Saynday. All the time the rocks were holding Saynday down. They went along and along till they got to Mt. Scott, and when they were around on the other side, Coyote threw his stick away, and stretched out along the ground like a racehorse. He flew back to the kettle of soup, and when he got there he sat down on the ground and he ate it all up.

Just as he finished, Saynday got there.

"Where's my soup?" said Saynday.

"I ate it all up," said Coyote.

"It was my soup," said Saynday.

"I raced you for it and won the race," said Coyote.

"It wasn't a fair race," whined Saynday.

"It was as fair as the way you got the soup in the first place," said Coyote.

And there Saynday was, and there he stayed, and he got no soup that day.

HOW SAYNDAY GOT CAUGHT IN A TREE

SAYNDAY WAS COMING ALONG, and as he came he saw a clump of wild cherry trees, the kind that the Indians call real fruit. He hurried up to the trees and began to stuff himself full of wild cherries.

"My," he said to himself, "here I am gobbling cherries like an old bear. Of course, my mouth isn't as big as a bear's, and my face isn't as ugly, but I am acting like one."

He went on eating big handfuls of wild cherries as fast as he could pick them.

"My hands aren't as big as a bear's paws, either," he said to himself. "Now that's something I wish I had. I would like to have great big ugly paws like a bear's, so I could pick more fruit at a time. And if I had a big ugly mouth like a bear's, I could eat a lot more fruit at a time. But, still," said Saynday to himself, "I'm glad I don't have to look like that old ugly thing."

And just then a bear stuck his head around the bush where Saynday was picking, and said, "Well! Are you there!"

Saynday was so surprised that he sat down backward on the ground on a prickly pear, and had to jump up again quicker than he sat down.

"Heard what you said," said Bear.

"Oh, dear," thought Saynday. He was too frightened to say anything.

"Heard what you said and didn't like it," said Bear.

"Oh, dear me!" thought Saynday.

"So I want to know what you're going to do about it," said Bear.

Saynday thought hard and Saynday thought fast, and then he said, "Did you ever pick wild cherries?"

"Yes," said Bear, who still had a few stems hanging out of one corner of his mouth.

"Well," said Saynday, "then you know how it is. You know how good they are. You can eat and eat, and it seems as if you never would get enough."

"That's right," said Bear, reaching out and gathering in an extra handful, now that Saynday reminded him.

"Well," went on Saynday, "if you were gathering wild cherries, and you happened to think of a friend who had fine big paws to pick a lot of cherries with, and a fine big mouth to eat a lot of cherries with, wouldn't you want to be like him?"

"That's all right," said Bear, "but that isn't what you were saying when I came up. You said then that my mouth and my paws were ugly."

"That's just because I was jealous," said Saynday. "You know how it is. The more envious you are, the worse you make things sound."

"Well, if that's the way it is," said Bear.

And they went on picking and eating side by side. Pretty soon Saynday got full up with wild cherries, and began to think about having something else to eat.

"Aren't you tired?" he asked Bear.

"Well, yes, I am," answered Bear, and he looked around for a place on the ground where there was no prickly pear, so he could sit down.

"I've just thought of a game," said Saynday.

"What sort of game?" asked Bear.

"Oh, a good game," said Saynday. "First we dig a hole."

"How big a hole?" asked Bear.

"Oh, a big hole. Big enough to get into."

"Both together or one at a time?" asked Bear, who liked to have things straight.

"Just one at a time," said Saynday.

"All right," said Bear.

And they went to work and dug a hole that they could get into one at a time.

"Now what?" said Bear.

"Now one of us gets into it," said Saynday. "Then the other one builds a fire on top of him. When the one in the hole gets hot enough, he calls out, 'My eyes are popping,' and the other one gets him out."

"Well," said Bear, "that sounds to me like a dangerous game."

"Oh, it's a fine game," said Saynday. "Just wait till you try it."

"All right," said Bear, "but you've got to get into the hole first."

"Well, all right," said Saynday. "That part's the most fun. I can hardly wait till I try it."

Saynday crawled into the hole, and Bear piled a big fire up around and over him, and lighted it.

Pretty soon Saynday decided that he'd been in that hole long enough. He felt as if he were almost roasted.

"My eyes are popping! My eyes are popping!" he yelled, and Bear scattered the fire around and let him out.

"Now it's your turn," said Saynday. And Bear said, "Did you really have a good time?"

"I had a fine time," said Saynday. "I had the best time I ever had in my life."

Then Bear was willing to get into the hole, and in he got. Saynday piled up a big fire around and over him, and lighted it.

Pretty soon Bear called out, "My eyes are popping! Oh, my eyes are popping right out of my head!"

"Let them pop!" said Saynday, and he crawled up into the fork of a big wild cherry tree and lay back against the trunk, watching his meat cook.

Because he was Saynday, and could never leave well enough alone, he began playing with the tree. He would say, "Tree, close in," and the forks of the tree would close in around him.

Then he would say, "Tree, open out," and the tree would spread its branches out wide.

Saynday sat there and smelled his meat cooking, and played with the tree, and waited for his dinner to get done. Magpie smelled the meat cooking, too, and came flying over to see what Saynday was doing.

"My, that's a big barbecue," said Magpie.

"Yes, it is," said Saynday, "and I'm going to eat it all up."

"All by yourself?" asked Magpie.

"All by myself with nobody helping me," said Saynday.

"I think you have enough to divide," said Magpie.

"No, I haven't," said Saynday. "I just have enough for me."

"You're selfish," said Magpie.

"I don't care if I am," said Saynday. "I caught that meat and I'm cooking that meat, and I'm not going to share it with anybody."

"All right," said Magpie, "I'll show you what that gets you! Tree, close in and hold him tight!"

And the wild cherry tree, which was getting pretty disgusted itself, closed in on Saynday, and held him tight. He struggled and fought and pleaded and begged, but the tree wouldn't let him go, even for a minute.

"Now," said Magpie, "you just stay there and

wait, and I'll show you what happens to greedy people."

Then Magpie went flying off and got his relatives. When he told them that Saynday was giving a big feast, they all came in a hurry. When they saw Saynday caught in the tree, they laughed so hard they could hardly eat for a while. But when they did start eating, they made up for lost time. They ate up every bit of the bear meat, and Saynday just had to sit there watching them.

"There," said Magpie when they had finished. "Now you see. Tree, open out and drop him."

Then the wild chery tree let Saynday go, and he fell with a thud to the ground. And there on the ground he had to lie, hungry and empty and worn out with fighting the tree.

HOW THE BOBCAT GOT HIS SPOTS

SAYNDAY WAS COMING ALONG, and as he came he saw a big piece of pounded meat rolling along the ground like a ball. She was traveling along bothering nobody, and singing a little song that went, "Loo-loo. Loo-loo."

"Well, now, that reminds me," Saynday said to himself, "I haven't had any dinner."

So he quickly ran around a little hill and lay down on the ground in the path of Pounded Meat. There he lay and sighed and groaned and groaned and sighed, and when Pounded Meat came to him she stopped to see what was making all that noise.

"Well, what is the trouble?" asked Pounded Meat.

"Oh," sighed Saynday, "I'm so hungry. So very hungry. I think I'm starving. I think I'm dying of starving."

"Oh," said Pounded Meat, "it can't be as bad as all that. People don't die of starving in less than a week, and you look as if you had something to eat the day before yesterday."

"Oh, no, I didn't," Saynday groaned. "I don't remember when I had anything to eat. It's so long ago that I've forgotten all about it. Oh, please, please give me a little bite off your arm, just to keep me living till morning. I'll take such a little bite that you won't ever miss it."

"Well, all right," said Pounded Meat, and she held out her arm and Saynday took a big chunk of a bite out of it.

"Well," said Pounded Meat, "I hope I can get used to missing that."

"Which way are you going?" asked Saynday.

"Right on down this road," said Pounded Meat.

"Oh, that's good," said Saynday. "That makes me so happy. Now I feel better."

Pounded Meat began to get a little nervous then.

"Why does that make you feel better?" she wanted to know.

"Because my poor brothers live along this road, and they are all starving to death, too," said Saynday.

Pounded Meat didn't like that very well, because she didn't want to get all eaten up, but she was headed down that road and she had to keep going.

"Well, goodbye," she said to Saynday.

Saynday said, "Goodbye. I'm VERY glad I met you."

As soon as she had gone off, rolling down the road, Saynday jumped up and ran as quickly as he could, and lay down in the road again ahead of her. Pretty soon Pounded Meat came rolling along, singing her little song under her breath, "Loo-loo. Loo-loo."

She came to where Saynday lay, and he groaned a little and stretched out his hand.

"I was afraid of this," said Pounded Meat.

"Oh," moaned Saynday, "I'm so hungry. I'm starving to death."

"That's what I heard," said Pounded Meat.

"Please," sighed Saynday, "please give me a little piece out of your leg. Just a very little piece. I'll take it from in back, from the fat part, where you won't ever miss it at all."

"Well, I don't know," said Pounded Meat. "Your brother who lives up the road told me almost the same thing. He said he would take a little piece out of my arm where I wouldn't miss it, but he took a big piece, and I haven't got used to missing it yet."

"I'm not greedy like my brother," said Saynday. "I'm a very unselfish man. But please, please give me a little bite out of your leg."

"All right," said Pounded Meat, and Saynday bit a big chunk out of her leg.

"Ouch!" said Pounded Meat. "That hurts. You weren't supposed to take a great big piece like that."

"Excuse me," said Saynday. "I was so hungry that I was careless. Oh, I'm so glad you are traveling down this road. My poor brothers live a little farther on, and they are all starving, too."

"How many are there of you?" asked Pounded Meat.

"I don't just remember," said Saynday. "We're a very large family."

He lay back on the ground and groaned some more, and Pounded Meat went rolling along singing her little song, "Loo-loo. Loo-loo."

Pretty soon she came to another starving Saynday stretched on the ground, for he'd run around another hill and got ahead of her again.

"Well," said Pounded Meat, "this is a large

family, and they all look alike, too." And she stopped to think things over.

Saynday moaned and groaned and sighed and sobbed, and Pounded Meat went up close to look at him.

"You seem to be worse off than your brothers," she said.

And Saynday answered, "Oh, I am, indeed I am. They had something to eat a week ago, but I haven't eaten in a month."

"Dear me," said Pounded Meat, bending over closer still. "That is very sad."

And she bent down so close she could see into his mouth. There she saw something sticking to his tooth. It was a little scrap of pounded meat.

"Well," said Pounded Meat, "is that a piece of my arm or my leg?"

And she bent down even closer and looked some more, and she recognized Saynday.

"Oh, my goodness," said Pounded Meat.

And she started to run as hard as she could. Saynday jumped up and ran after her, racing along so fast that Pounded Meat really had to tear, and she forgot all about singing her little song, "Loo-loo. Loo-loo."

Saynday chased Pounded Meat along the flat and up the rise and down the hill, and at the bottom of the hill she rolled into a little pond and drowned.

"Now," said Saynday, "I'm going to have a real dinner. I'll start with some soup."

So he built a fire and got ready to cook his meat in the old-fashioned Indian way. First he let the fire burn bright, and then he let it die down to hot coals, and then he rolled stones on the coals. When the stones were red hot, he picked them up one at a time with a forked stick, and dropped them into the pond to heat the water. When he had a lot of red-hot stones in the pond, the water began to bubble and boil, and Saynday's soup was cooking. After a while it was done.

Then Saynday got ready to eat it, and he found he had no spoon.

"Oh, dear," he said, "I'm here and the soup's here, but the spoon's at home. I guess I'll have to go home and get the spoon."

It was getting dark by that time, and Bobcat, who never gets up till the sun goes down, came along. It was just about his breakfast time, and he was as hungry as Saynday.

"That smells good," said Bobcat.

"I guess it is good," said Saynday.

"Why don't we eat it and find out?" said Bobcat.

"We aren't going to eat it," said Saynday. "I'm going to eat it."

Bobcat had his own ideas about that, but he didn't argue.

Instead he said, "Why don't you eat it, then?"

"I can't," said Saynday. "My spoon's at home."

"Why don't you go and get it?" asked Bobcat.

"I'm afraid somebody will come along and steal my soup," said Saynday.

"I'll watch it for you," said Bobcat. "Nobody will bother it while I'm here."

And he climbed up in the branches of a big cottonwood tree that hung out over the pond, and settled down to watch the soup.

"All right," said Saynday. "You stay there and watch it while I get the spoon, and if there's any left over I'll give you some."

And he went on off.

As soon as Saynday was gone, Bobcat climbed down out of the tree, and started lapping the soup out of the pond. He ate and he ate till he couldn't eat any more, but there was still a little soup left in the bottom. Just then he heard Saynday coming back, so he climbed back up in his tree and stretched out on a limb, looking at his big fat full reflection in the pond below him.

Saynday came running up with his spoon, and then he saw that his soup was all gone.

"Oh, my beautiful soup!" he howled. "What has become of my beautiful soup? Someone has eaten it all up!"

Then he saw Bobcat's reflection in the pond.

"There's the one!" Saynday cried. "There's the bad one who ate up all my soup!"

And he picked up stones from the bank of the pond and began throwing them at Bobcat's reflection. He threw harder and harder and the water and the soup and the mud splashed higher and higher till it spotted Bobcat's fur, where he was lying in the tree. Saynday looked up and saw him, with the dirt spots all over his clean yellow coat.

"There!" said Saynday, "that's good enough for you. You can just go on wearing those spots for always, to show people what a soup stealer you are."

And that's the way it was, and that's the way it is, to this good day.

HOW SAYNDAY TRIED TO MARRY THE WHIRLWIND

SAYNDAY WAS COMING ALONG, and as he came he saw a beautiful girl. She was so beautiful he stopped dead in his tracks to admire her.

"Oh, my," said Saynday, "how lovely you are! What is your name and where did you come from? I never saw anything so beautiful!"

"My name is Whirlwind," said the girl, "and I came out of the south and the west with the heat of midsummer."

"Whirlwind, Whirlwind," said Saynday. "That's a pretty name. It's as pretty as the rest of you. Look here, I think we ought to get married."

"Oh," said Whirlwind, "I don't want to marry you. You have funny arms and funny legs and a funny voice, and that queer mustache in the middle of your face."

"I'm very goodhearted," said Saynday. "The way I look doesn't have a thing to do with that."

"Well," said Whirlwind, "I really don't want to marry anybody. I'm too young to get married."

"Oh, no, you're not," said Saynday. "You're just right to get married. Anyone as beautiful as you are ought to get married right away while she's young, before she gets old and fat and ugly, and nobody will have her."

"I still don't know," said Whirlwind. The more she looked at him, the less she wanted to marry Saynday. "My people say I'm very hard to get along with. Maybe I'd better not marry anybody."

"Well, I'm not easy to get along with myself," said Saynday. "Some people say I'm just mean, because I'm so hard to get along with. That ought to make us a good pair."

"Of course," said Whirlwind, "when I really like somebody, I'm willing to do a lot to get along with him." She had thought of a plan to make Saynday sorry he'd ever even seen her.

"That's just the way I am," said Saynday. "Why, I'd do anything to make a person I really loved happy."

"Well," said Whirlwind, "you make us sound a lot alike."

"Oh, we are," said Saynday. "I think we'd be making a big mistake not to get married. It seems to me we're just made for each other!"

"All right," said Whirlwind, "I guess we should, then."

Saynday was so excited he came running at her with his eyes shut and his arms open to catch her and hold her, so she couldn't change her mind and run away. Just as he caught hold of her, up she went in a cloud of leaves and grass and sticks and trash, carrying Saynday along with her.

She carried him away and away, and then she threw him down on the ground by Saddle Mountain.

"There!" she said. "Maybe that'll teach you a lesson. Maybe now you'll believe what a person tells you the first time!"

And she went off and left him choking and spluttering in her dust, for she really was the whirlwind.

INDIAN SAYNDAY AND WHITE
MAN SAYNDAY

SAYNDAY WAS COMING ALONG, and as he came he saw a white man. The white man was all dressed up in a twenty-gallon Stetson hat, and a buckskin vest with all sorts of fancy designs beaded on it. He had buckskin riding gloves with long fringes, and chaps made out of bobcat hide, and a pair of handmade cowboy boots. He was riding a fine buckskin horse with a white mane and tail, the kind they call a palomino. And he and the horse were really carrying on, because they knew they looked so fine.

Saynday stopped and stood and looked them all over.

"Well," he said to himself, "that's the kind of outfit I'd like to have."

So he walked over toward the white man with the fine palomino horse and the good clothes, and he said, "What's your name?"

"Saynday," said the white man.

"Saynday?" said Saynday. "Why, that's not

your name. That can't be your name. That's an Indian name."

"White Man Saynday," said the white man.

"Is that so?" said Indian Saynday. "Well, my name's Saynday, too. I'm Indian Saynday."

"Well," said White Man Saynday, "is that the truth? I've been hearing a lot about you. You don't look like a man people would talk much about."

He looked at Indian Saynday, who wasn't wearing anything but some old moccasins and an old breechclout. He looked funnier even than usual.

"Yes," said Indian Saynday. "I'm the Indians' old Uncle Saynday. I'm the man that's always coming along."

"Well," said White Man Saynday, "now you've come up with me."

"I certainly have," said Indian Saynday. "That's a fine suit of clothes you've got."

"Oh, it's just an old everyday suit," said White Man Saynday. "I got it out of a Montgomery Ward catalog."

"I thought it looked pretty fine," said Indian Saynday. "That's a fine horse you've got, too."

White Man Saynday didn't say anything to run

down his horse, because he knew it was the best there was.

"I hear you play tricks on people," he said.

Indian Saynday answered, "Oh, yes, I play lots of tricks on people. I play tricks on almost everybody."

"Don't your tricks ever go wrong?" asked White Man Saynday.

"Oh, once in a while," said Indian Saynday. "Not very often, though. I'm pretty good."

"Well," said White Man Saynday, "I've been wanting to meet you. I bet you can't play a trick on me."

"Well, I don't know whether I could right now," said Indian Saynday.

"Oh, go on," said White Man Saynday. "I bet you can't."

"I couldn't right now," said Indian Saynday. "You know how Indians are. They have to have their medicine-power things handy to do anything. I have medicine-power things for doing tricks on people, but I haven't got them right here with me. Now, if I had them, I could play all kinds of tricks on you, but I can't do a thing without them."

"You're just making that up," said White Man Saynday. "Why, I bet you haven't any more got medicine-power things than I have. You're just trying to get out of working tricks on me because you know you can't."

"No, I'm not," said Indian Saynday. "It's just that I have to have those things to work any tricks on anybody. I'm just helpless without them."

"Well, where are those wonderful things?" asked White Man Saynday.

"They're at home," said Indian Saynday.

"Where is your home?" said White Man Saynday.

"Over there," said Indian Saynday, jerking his chin to point with it.

"Is it far?" asked White Man Saynday.

"Not very far," said Indian Saynday. "It's pretty far, too."

"How far?" White Man Saynday wanted to know.

"Well, pretty far," said Indian Saynday. "Too far to walk."

"Why don't you ride?" said White Man Saynday.

"I haven't any horse," said Indian Saynday. "How's a poor Indian going to get a horse?"

"You could buy one," said White Man Saynday.

"How's a poor Indian going to get any money?" asked Indian Saynday.

"Well, I tell you," said White Man Saynday, "I surely do want to see you work some of your tricks. I've heard about them and heard about them, about how good they are and how smart you are, and I want to see you try it. I want to see you try it so much that I'll lend you my horse so you can go and get your medicine-power things."

"That's nice of you," said Indian Saynday, edging up toward the fine palomino horse, "but I guess you'd better not. I'd like to borrow that horse to ride, all right, but it's too good a horse. You wouldn't want to risk letting a poor Indian ride it."

"Oh, I don't care," said White Man Saynday. "It's a rodeo horse. You may ride him if you can hold him."

"Well," said Indian Saynday, sounding pretty doubtful, "I can try."

White Man Sayday got down off the horse, and Indian Sayday went over and took the bridle. That fine palomino horse was all trimmed up with a silver-plated saddle, and a silver bridle, and an Indian saddle blanket, and two pistols with silver-and-ivory handles. The trappings were just as fine as the horse.

"My," said Indian Sayday, "these are fine trappings. Don't you want to take them off the horse before I ride him?"

White Man Sayday was getting very impatient now.

"Go on," he said. "Get on the horse," he said, "and go and get your medicine-power things. If you don't, I won't believe you have any power at all."

"All right," said Indian Sayday.

He swung up in the saddle on the left-hand side of the horse, like a white man, but as he swung up he pushed that fine palomino horse in the side with his knee. And the fine palomino horse jumped over sidewise and started to buck as if he had a bur under his saddle.

"There!" said Indian Sayday. "I was afraid of that. He doesn't want a stranger to ride him. We'll just have to let the medicine-power things go."

"He never acts up like that with me," said White Man Saynday.

"Well, of course not," said Indian Saynday. "He's used to you. He's used to the way you're dressed, and the shape of your hat and chaps. But I haven't got on any clothes, let alone any hat and chaps, so he's scared of me."

"Maybe that's it," said White Man Saynday. "Here, you take my clothes. Put them on. Then he won't know the difference."

"I don't think I ought to do that," said Indian Saynday. "I might ruin your fine clothes that you got out of the catalog. No, I don't think that's a good idea at all."

White Man Saynday was getting more and more impatient.

"I can't sit around here all day, waiting to be tricked," he said. "If you think you can trick me, all well and good. If you don't, just say so and go on about your business."

"Oh, I think I can trick you, all right," said Indian Saynday, "if I just once get my hands on my Indian medicine-power things."

"Well, that's the way it is," said White Man Saynday. "You put on my clothes and get on my horse, and go and get those Indian medicine-power things of yours, and be quick about it."

"All right," said Indian Saynday. "You just don't know how you're going to be tricked!"

They left the fine palomino horse with his reins dragging, and White Man Saynday began taking off his fine clothes. As fast as he took them off, Indian Saynday put them on. He put on the hat and the chaps and the boots and the breeches and the vest and the shirt and the gauntlets. He put on everything that White Man Saynday had, and he left White Man Saynday with the old moccasins and the breechclout that he'd been wearing himself. When he got all dressed up, Indian Saynday certainly looked fine.

"All right," he said to White Man Saynday. "Are you quite sure you want to do this?"

"I'm sure," said White Man Saynday.

So Indian Saynday walked over to the fine palomino, and gathered up the reins, and flew himself into the saddle. He got all settled, and shook the reins, and the horse started to gallop, away and away, off towards Mt. Scott.

And Indian Saynday looked back over his shoulder, and yelled at White Man Saynday, "You wanted to see the way I trick people. Well, that's how I do it!"

THE END OF SAYNDAY

WHEN SAYNDAY HAD FINISHED all his good work and all his bad work in this world, he called all his friends together, just at sundown. They all came: Deer and Magpie and Dragonfly and Coyote, and even the prairie dogs, and Bobcat, and Old Spider Woman. They all stood around Saynday, and listened to him.

"Here is my world," he said, "all ready for you to live in. I've fixed it up, and made it just as nice as I can. There's just one more thing I'm going to fix. Over there in the east, on the rim of the sky as the sun goes down, there's a space without any stars."

He stretched out his hand, away and away to the east, and five bright stars came out on the rim of the sky, one for each of his fingers.

"Now, that's where I'm going," said Saynday. "Up there where the fingers of my hand are. All summer long you will see my hand up there at sundown. Then you will know that I am watching out for things that are living and growing in my world, and as long as I'm watching you there from the east, you mustn't tell my stories. But when winter comes and you can't see my hand, then you will know that I am resting, and then's when my stories can be told. Now I am going away. Goodbye."

And before they could look or know, he was gone, with nothing but his hand in the sky to show that he was still watching over them.

And that's the way it was, and that's the way it is, to this good day.

INDIANS ON HORSEBACK

For MOLLY
because we went to Gallup

Drawings by Margaret Lefranc

1

WHO THE PLAINS INDIANS ARE

THE FIRST HOME of the Plains Indians probably was on the plains, or steppes, of Siberia and northern Asia. There they fished and hunted and traveled, moving eastward little by little, till they came to the shores of a great sea. A long hook of rock stuck out from the mainland, stretching out across the water as far as the people could see. There was game on the land and there were fish in the ocean, so the people moved out on the land hook, still fishing and hunting and traveling.

In summer, this new land that they were crossing very slowly and through many years, was covered with short grass and small flowers. There were few bushes and no trees, but the travelers could have found driftwood that had washed ashore where they were fishing. From the driftwood the people probably built fires for cooking and to keep themselves warm.

The sea froze over in winter, and both fish and land

game were scarce in the cold weather. Maybe some of the men learned to fish through holes in the ice, but those who went hunting must have found little game. So the people moved on as quickly as they could, still going forward, since they had come too far now to turn back. In time the land broadened out before them, and the people found themselves in Alaska, and on the new continent of North America.

All this traveling happened a long time ago. Some scientists say that it was as long ago as twenty thousand years. At least it all happened before the continent of North America was completely formed, and at the time when it was still settling itself into shape. Not very long after the people had journeyed over the land bridge from Siberia, across what we call the Bering Sea, the hook-shaped bridge sank into the ocean, and the travelers were cut off from their old homes in Asia.

When these people first crossed to North America, they all did things in much the same ways. They all fished and hunted, and they all used fire. They all made ropes and cords by twisting strands of bark or sinew fiber together. They all hunted with spears; and they all had tame dogs, probably to help them with the hunting. We know that these people did these things because all the Indians in

North and South America have always done them. They cannot remember a time when their tribes lacked these customs and possessions.

So far as we know, these travelers were the first people to come to North America, and they found no one there before them. After they were all alone in the new land, the people began to separate into groups of families and friends. They did not form big groups, because it was still hard for them to find food. Many people living close together could use up the fish and game quickly. As they had done before, the new family groups hunted and traveled and fished. Game was most plentiful in the south, and the country there was open. So, because it was the easiest way to go, they moved southward, on the inland side of the coastal mountains.

In time, they came to a place where the land opened out to the south and east of them, and, as far as they could see, there was an open space like an ocean of land. This was the Great Plains, where the land rolls like waves or lies flat like calm water; where there are few trees and no mountains to break the earth's surface. Rivers and streams cross the plains, but even the Mississippi and Missouri look small compared to the size of the land around them.

There they stood, those little groups of families. They looked out at the great sweep of prairie and were afraid to step onto it, for they had no way of telling what it held or where it ended. So the people camped and made settlements along the edges of the plains, and after a time hunting parties dared to go out onto the sea of grass. Once the hunters were out upon its surface, they found the biggest animal they had ever known. This was the bison, or American buffalo. A full-grown animal weighed as much as half a ton, and had enough good meat on its bones to feed a hungry family for a long time.

This, then, was good country for the hunters. The people built their camps as near the streams as they could. Some of them learned to make small houses out of willow or cottonwood branches, and some of them used the skins of the buffalo they killed to make cone-shaped tents. The people who lived near the big Missouri River made boats out of the buffalo skins, so that they could travel on the river. All the Indians, when they wanted to travel overland, tied poles to the backs of their dogs, letting the ends of the poles drag on the ground. Then the people piled their tents and clothes and household goods on racks tied between the poles. Because it is easier to drag a load than to carry it, the dogs were able to take the heaviest burdens, leaving the men free to hunt and the women able to care for their children while they traveled.

All these changes had taken a long time to happen. Most of the twenty thousand years were gone by now, and it was 1540 in our way of reckoning time. Away and away to the south other strangers had come to the continent. This time they came from the east. These men were the Spanish. Unlike the Indians, they came planning to settle in one place in the new country. They brought with them many of the things they were used to living with at home in Spain.

The most important and most wonderful things the Spaniards brought, to the Indians' eyes, were their horses. These were animals almost as big and strong as the buffalo, and faster running. On the backs of the horses rode the soldiers in armor, and when the Indians first saw a man dismount, they thought the animal had split itself in two. That made the new animals seem even more wonderful than the Indians had first thought them to be. In time, the Indians learned that the riders were men like themselves. Soon many of the Indians began to believe that if they had horses they, too, could ride.

It took a long time for the Indians to get horses from the Spaniards. A few of the horses were bought for painted hides, and dried meat, and tools and weapons which the Spanish needed. Some of the horses ran away from their owners, and the Indians caught them and kept them. Some of the Indians wanted horses so badly that they crept at night into the Spanish camps and took the horses away with them. In all these ways the Indians were able to get what they called "the wonderful big dogs."

Then all of a sudden a strange thing happened. The Indians found that they were no longer afraid of the great oceanlike grassland on whose edges they lived. The Indians themselves could ride out across the prairies, high enough, when they were on horseback, to see over the tall grasses and to find the buffalo herds that were still far away. It was like finding another new continent; it was like being set free. With this discovery, that they could move around easily on horseback, the Indians began a new way of life.

The Indians soon found out, too, that there were many more buffalo on the plains than they had thought. There was one great herd in the northern plains and another in the south. The herds moved from place to place, looking for fresh grass and clear water, and there were so many buffalo in each herd that it took them many days to pass a single place. With their horses, the Indians could follow the buffalo herds. They could be sure of getting meat whenever they needed it, instead of having to chance hunting without getting any game.

Not all of the Indian tribes dared to make the adventure of living out on the plains. Along the northern edges of the grasslands there still lived the Dog Knives and the

Babiche and the Tanaina; in the east were the Sauk and the Fox, the Winnebago and the Pottawatomie. Along the western edge of the plains were the Navajo and the Pueblos and the Paviotso; and in the south were the Kichai and the Tawakoni and the Wichita. None of these tribes tried the new kind of life. There were many others, too, who continued to live as they had before, but it would make too long a list to name them all.

But these are the names of some of the tribes who began the new way of living as soon as they got horses: the Cheyenne and the Arapaho; the Mandan, the Hidatsa and the Ute; the Crow and the Shoshoni; the Sioux, or Dakota; the Kiowa and the Comanche and the Jicarilla Apache; the Blackfeet and the Flatheads and the Piegan. Everyone of these tribes had its own different language, as well as its own special name.

Then the tribes who went out on the plains began to think of their whole lives in terms of moving. They had horses, so they could travel quickly and easily. They had horses, and the horses could carry heavier burdens than dogs. They had horses, so they could find, and outrun, and kill, much game.

All this meant that these Indians gave up or threw away whatever they had that was heavy or hard to take with them on their horses. They no longer built shelters out of brush and tree limbs, but all of them learned to make light tents, or teepees, out of buffalo hides. Some of the tribes, such as the Cheyenne and the Hidatsa, who had once made baskets and pottery, stopped working at these crafts. Like the other plains people, they learned to make all their containers out of skins. All their clothing was made of skins, too, for weaving took a long time, and weaving-frames were hard to carry with them.

Thus these tribes became what we call the Plains Indians; hunters, who sometimes fought each other fiercely over the buffalo herds, and who made a game of raiding each others' horses. Because they were hunters and fighters they became fine weapon makers. Their bows and arrows were short in order to be more easily used on horseback. The Plains tribes made short throwing and thrusting spears too, with which a man on horseback could strike quickly and surely.

But the Plains Indians did not fight chiefly to kill. They fought to defend their lands; to drive out intruders; and to show their personal bravery. They thought it took greater courage to touch an armed man than to kill him, and the man who most often touched his enemies with his bare hand or his short spear, in battle, was considered the bravest in his group or tribe. War was like a game to the Plains Indians; not like a battle as we think of battles.

Their lives were not all made up of hunting and fighting. When there were no enemies around, and there was food enough in the teepee for everyone to eat, the men had time to make religious songs and ceremonies. Some of these songs are still sung; and some of the ceremonies are still performed. Women took part in a few of the ceremonies, which were really long prayers in the form of dances and songs.

Most of the time, though, the women were busy with other work. The women tanned the hides that the men brought home from hunting, and cut and sewed teepees and clothing from the tanned skins. They made moccasins for foot covering, and painted designs on them with earth colors. They dried the buffalo meat and then pounded it with stone hammers. The finely powdered meat they mixed with fat and berries and stored away for winter use. The women did not work as hard at any one time as the men did when they were hunting, but the women's work went on steadily every day.

The children learned to do as their elders did, for most of their games were imitation work. They played camping and hunting and fighting; and the little girls played with dolls and at keeping house. There were other games, too. The children slid on the ice, or skated on it with skates made of buffalo rib bones, in the winter. Sometimes they made cats' cradles of string, when the weather was too cold for them to go outdoors.

Old men and women were the rememberers of their tribes. They kept the history of what had happened in their minds, usually, for they had no way of writing. Sometimes, though, the old men drew pictures of the histories on hides, as reminders of the things that had happened and the way the events took place. And the old people remembered, too, and told to the children long stories and legends about gods and spirits and tribal heroes. All the stories were important to everybody, but only the old people had time enough to think a great deal about them.

2

WHAT THE GREAT PLAINS ARE

A CONTINENT actually is made like a saucer. It is turned up, with mountains around its edges; and in the middle it is lower and almost flat. All continents have this same kind of shape, and North America is no exception. Its east and west rims are the Appalachian and the Rocky mountains, while in the middle it slopes downward to a center called the Great Plains.

We usually think of plains as flat areas, although they are not really flat. The surface of the plain curves with the curve of the earth. When you stand in the middle of this space, there is a circle of sky all around you, and you seem to be standing on a little rise. Whether you move north or south or east or west, if you are in the true Great Plains, the place where you stop will always seem to be a little higher than the land around you.

But the great surface of this earth curve is not actually

smooth. It is cut through by rivers, which dig their beds lower than the country around them. Where there had been rivers and lakes formed by these rivers in times past, the earth is low. On the banks of the rivers and the shores of the long-ago lakes the ground is high.

Where the earth is bare, the wind and the rain cut it up into hills with sharp, almost straight, sides. These hills are called bluffs. Where the bluffs are left standing alone, the wind and rain cut more deeply into their sides, and buttes and mesas are formed. To look at a plain from near by is to see all these shapes which time and the weather have left, and to wonder how the plains ever came to be called flat.

Away from the rivers and the trees that grow on their banks, the plains are usually covered with grass. Sometimes this is short grass, but it may grow to be "knee high to a man on a horse," as the cowboys used to say. As long as the grass cover grows, the plains look flatter than they really are, for the grass evens off little surface bumps and hollows, and holds the soil in place.

When the grass is plowed up and the soil of the plains is broken, water runs along the lower places during the rains, and in the dry seasons the wind runs along them like the water. Both water and wind cut away the soil, so

that more and more the plains are broken up, and more
and more of their surface looks like the ground along the
rivers and beside the old lakes. New rivers and lakes form
in the new low places, and as their banks grow higher
and higher, new bluffs and buttes are made. All these
things are going on today. The Great Plains are always
changing, like a great ocean.

The Great Plains of North America start almost at the
Arctic Circle. They stretch south through central
Canada, and on south, between the Rocky Mountains
and the Mississippi River, into Mexico. Almost a third
of the United States lies within the Great Plains area.
Our plains states are Nebraska, the two Dakotas, Minne-
sota, Montana, Wyoming, Iowa, Illinois, Indiana, Mis-

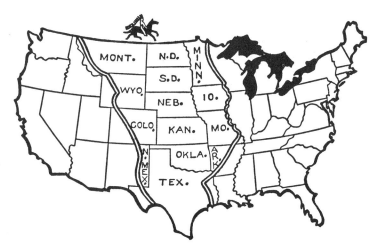

souri, Kansas, Arkansas, Oklahoma, and Texas. These
are some of the biggest states, as a group, in the Union,
and they make up a great stretch of country that is one
or the finest places in the world for growing grain and
raising cattle.

The climate of the Great Plains varies a good deal.
The coldest place in the United States is in northern North Dakota. There the temperature sometimes
drops to as low as 50 degrees below zero in the winter.
The highest temperature ever recorded in southern Texas
was 130 degrees above zero, in summer. In between these
two states are places with moderate temperatures all
the year round, and sections where the temperature rises
and falls a great deal during the year.

The rainfall of the plains varies less than the temperature does. Generally speaking, the plains area has
spring and fall rains, and some winter snow. In summer
the weather is usually dry. It is this alternation of wet and
dry seasons during the year that makes grain crops easy
to raise.

This is the weather of average years. In some years
the rains do not fall, and then, especially in the western
plains, there are long periods of droughts and dust
storms. In other years, the rains fall too heavily. Then

there are heavy floods, especially in the eastern plains. Both droughts and floods are destructive, not only to growing crops, but to the land itself. The wind and the rain cut deep into the soil and carry it away, hurrying the formation of buttes and mesas where once there were flat areas.

Nowadays, many of the people of the plains are white men, whose ancestors came to this country from Europe. Most of them came from the northern European countries: Sweden and Denmark and Norway; Belgium and Germany; England and Ireland and Scotland. They came looking for rich soil where their crops could grow, and where they could support themselves and their families.

They came to the new land, hard workers from hard countries, knowing that here they would have to work hard, too. They built cities and schools and churches and colleges; they have earned what they have and they are proud of what they have built.

Long before these white people came, the other peoples moved into the plains from Asia, to the west. They, too, made a way of life of which they were proud and which they loved. It is their story that this book is going to tell.

3

WHEN THE WHITE MEN CAME

WHILE THE LIFE of the Indians was changing, and the tribes were moving onto the plains, the white men's life was changing, too. More and more white people came into the plains country after about 1850. When they looked at the great flat prairies, the white men thought of the grasslands as places to grow corn and wheat and other grains. The newcomers began to root up the prairie grasses and plow up the earth so that they might plant their crops. So that the planted fields could grow, the white men drove away the buffalo, and fenced their lands to keep out the wild animals. When the buffalo came back to graze on the young grain, the white men killed the big animals to protect their lands and crops.

So that they could move about in the new country, the white men began building railroads across the plains. Soon they learned that the buffalo interfered with railroad traffic as much as they did with the crops. Sometimes a train had to wait for four days until one of the great buffalo herds had passed a certain place. In order that the trains could go through, the white men hired buffalo hunters to shoot the herds.

The hunters went to work in 1870, and by 1872 the two great buffalo herds were almost gone. Their hides were piled higher than the eaves of the railroad stations, where they were stored to be shipped east and made into shoe leather in Boston and other cities. The bones of the buffalo lay drying on the prairies, covering miles of country, and looking as if snow had fallen there in midsummer. So quickly were the herds wiped out that the Indians could not believe that the buffalo had been killed by men. To explain what had happened, the Plains Indians told each other that the buffalo had gone underground, and would hide there till all the white men were gone. Someday, the Indians said, the buffalo would come back, and life on the plains would be again as it was before.

These were hard times for the Plains Indians. The buffalo were what they lived on. Without the buffalo, the Indians starved and suffered. To protect their own and their children's lives, the Plains Indians tried to drive the white men away. But the white people did not fight like the Indians. The whites, too, were fighting to protect their lives and their way of living them, and they fought to kill.

Because the white settlers had guns, which were better weapons than bows and arrows, they finally won. After 1870, the white soldiers began to shut the Indians up on small areas of land, called reservations, and to hold them there. There was little food for the Indians to eat, and they had no room to go hunting. Even if they could have gone, there was almost no game left for them to bring home. Until the Plains Indians had learned to live on a small plot of land apiece, like the white farmers, they could hardly live at all. They had to give up many of their songs and ceremonies. The Indian children no longer played games, for the games they had known had no meaning any more. All the Indian life was changed.

It is of the times when the Indians were still living in their old way, before the white people settled on the plains in the 1800's, that we are going to talk now.

4

ONE MAN'S LIFE ON THE PLAINS

IN THE EARLY DAYS, when a Plains Indian baby was born, his grandmother was usually the first person to take care of him. She took the baby and rubbed him all over with warm, melted fat from a deer or from a buffalo cow. This was to make the baby's skin soft and smooth. It kept him clean, too, as soap does. Next the grandmother wrapped the baby in little, soft-tanned rabbit or squirrel skins, and then she put him in his cradle.

Some Plains Indian tribes had two kinds of cradles. The first kind, into which the new baby was put, and where most babies slept at night until they were about two years old, was very simple. This cradle was just a tube of buffalo hide, not worked and rubbed, or tanned, to make it soft; but sun dried, so it would be stiff. Hide prepared in this way was called rawhide. It had an unfinished surface that felt a little like blotting paper, and it took paints made of earth colors easily. The women painted sharp-edged designs, like diamonds and triangles, on the cradles with blue and red and yellow earths.

The second kind of cradle was harder to make. First, the grandmother whittled out flat boards, of bois d'arc or of cedar wood. The whittling took a long time because the only tool the old lady had was a knife. When the boards were flat and smooth, the grandmother pointed their top ends and rounded off the bottom ones. Then the finished boards were about three and a half feet long, four inches wide, and half an inch thick.

Next, the grandmother made a bag, or case, of soft-tanned deer hide. She bent a curved piece of buffalo rawhide across the top of the cradle, from one board to the other. Then she stretched the soft skin bag over the boards and the rawhide. She tied the bag tightly at the bottom, where the baby's feet would rest. She fastened the case to the back boards with rawhide strings. Last of all, she lined the case with small, soft skins and laid the baby inside. She covered him over with other soft little hides, instead of with sheets and blankets.

This was a good cradle. It was made in this way so that the baby would always be safe, even if the cradle were accidentally dropped or fell when the mother was busy.

If the cradle, with the baby in it, fell headfirst, even from a horse, the sharply pointed ends of the boards would stick in the ground and hold there. The baby would be upside down, and he would probably yell, but he would be safe and unhurt. If the cradle fell feet first, it would rock back and forth on the curved lower ends of the boards, and finally rest on its side. If the cradle fell on its back, the boards and the soft skin mattress would protect the baby's spine; and, if the cradle fell face forward, the curved rawhide hood would protect the baby's face. No matter what the mother was doing, riding or walking or working, she could feel sure that her baby would not be easily hurt.

A Plains Indian child spent most of his first two years in his cradle. Several times a day the baby's mother or grandmother would take him out; wash him; and rub his legs and arms with fat to keep them clean and to make them grow straight and supple. Sometimes the father or grandfather would take the baby out of the cradle. Then he would hold the child on his lap, and let him stretch and kick and grow. But during all the hours when the grown-ups were busy, the baby was in his cradle, which was hung from a teepee pole or tied to the horn of the mother's saddle. The baby could watch everything that went on around him and still be safe and out of the way. Often the baby was so comfortable and happy in his cradle that he cried when he was taken out of it.

After the baby had learned to walk, he was taught that there were some places where he should not go. He must not go near the horses, or near the places where the young men were dancing, or practicing with their bows and arrows. The best and safest place for a small child was inside the teepee or right in front of the doorway, and he was taught to play there until he was about four years old.

During these years, when the family traveled, the little child was tied on a bundle made of the teepee cover. The cover was tied to the teepee poles, and the whole load was fastened to the back of an old gentle mare, in the same way that smaller drags had once been fastened to the backs of the dogs. Sometimes, on a trip, the child's father would hold him in his arms on horseback, or would even put the small boy in front of him on the saddle, so the boy could get used to riding and to the feel of the horse.

When he was about six years old, a child learned to ride alone. At that age, a boy was given his first tiny bow and arrows, and a girl was given her first doll. The children played with their toys, but it was more than playing. A child was told that if he were old enough to have things of his own, he was old enough to take care of them and to use them in the right way. All the children tried to follow this good advice.

A boy was about six when he joined his first club, too. This was called the Rabbit Society, and it was for dancing

Rabbit Society Dance

and feasting and fun. All the little boys in the tribe belonged, and all of them took part in whatever their society did. Always in the summer, and sometimes during the winter months, the parents gave feasts for the boys. The children danced before they ate their dinner. When they danced, the boys hopped up and down, first on one foot and then on the other, and they flopped their hands up and down, like rabbits' ears, over their heads. The little girls danced, too. They formed a straight line behind their brothers and danced sidewise, with short steps. This was the same dancing step that the grown women used. After the dancing, the children feasted. If there were any food left over after they had eaten, the boys threw it at the girls and at each other. Sometimes all the children went home coated with meat and soup and dried berries.

A boy belonged to the Rabbit Society until he was about twelve. Then he joined another club, which was sometimes called the Herders' Society. From that time on the boy began to be grown up. He went out with the other boys, to watch the horse herds and to keep them from straying away from the main camp. If a boy's family had several horses, his parents gave him a horse of his own, so that he would learn how to take care of it. Instead of playing around camp with a toy bow and arrows, he was given a real set, strong enough to shoot a deer, and was taken along when the men went hunting.

The most exciting thing that happened to a Plains Indian boy was his first buffalo hunt. He remembered it always, even after he got to be an old man.

Early in the morning, the camp announcers went about, calling out for all the men who wanted to go hunting to get food for their families to come to a certain teepee. The men came from their own teepees, each wearing nothing but a breechclout and a pair of moccasins. Buffalo hunting was hard work, and clothes could get in the men's way. Every man carried his bow and arrows, and had a strong, sharp knife tied to the belt that held up his breechclout.

When all the men were ready, the one who had been elected head of the game wardens for that hunt told them what they were to do. He told every man where to ride, and warned them all to keep quiet until they came to the buffalo herd. He talked to them like a football coach before a game. He was always particularly careful to tell the young boys not to get excited; not to ride out ahead of the grown men; and not to yell. If anyone did such things, he might scare the buffalo away. Then he would be forbidden to hunt for a long time, until he learned to behave better.

The men and boys rode out of camp, then, just at dawn. They had to get started early, for buffalo hunting was no work for a lazy man. Along the edges of the plains the earth and the sky would melt and run and be stuck together with a little bit of mist. When the sun came up, first there would be color in the sky and then shapes on the earth—the long shapes of men and horses spreading out on the grass. The men rode bareback and the horses were unshod, so there were few sounds. The only movements besides those of the horses were the signals of the game wardens.

When the hunters came to the buffalo herd, they stopped and sat still. Then the head of the game wardens brought his right hand up above his head and down straight to his side. That was the signal for the men to ride into the herd and start shooting. When the signal came, all the hunters kicked their horses forward into a gallop. The riders stretched out as far forward over the horses' heads as they could reach, and shot as hard and as fast as they knew how. Afterwards a man could tell which buffalo he had shot because his arrows were painted with his own design.

The First Buffalo Hunt

The shooting was over very quickly. Almost as soon as the hunters charged, the buffalo ran away. Only the dead and wounded animals were left. Sometimes a buffalo that had been shot but not killed would charge at a man and try to kill him. Then the man would ride away if he could, but if he could not escape, all the hunters would try to shoot that one buffalo and save the man. Afterward the hunters decided whose arrow had struck the animal first. If they couldn't agree, the game wardens divided the meat from the buffalo among all the hunters whose arrows had hit it.

The women followed when the men went hunting. When the shooting was over, the women came up with pack horses, to help with skinning and cutting up the meat. The women helped with this part of the work because they knew what they wanted to use the buffalo hides for, and how to get them off the best way for that purpose. Both men and women knew the best ways of cutting up the meat.

If a boy had shot his first buffalo in a hunt, his father cut out the tongue and gave it to him. The tongue was thought to be the best part of the meat. The boy gave the tongue to some of the older people who were not his relatives. To give something in this way was called a "give-away," and it was done in this case to teach the boy to be generous and to help those around him. The boy himself did not eat any meat from his first buffalo. This was to teach him not to be greedy, nor to want to get things for himself alone. In this way he learned to want to work for his family.

When he was fourteen or fifteen, a Plains Indian boy went on his first war raid. He did not take part in the fighting, unless he were in great danger and had to defend himself. Instead, he cooked for the older men and cared for their horses. He brought the men water and ran errands for them. All the time he was watching what the older people did and learning what to do himself, when the time came.

As we have already said, the Plains Indians did not make war primarily to kill one another. Most of the tribes went on raids to get horses or to take captives. Sometimes two tribes would fight over who should have the area where a certain buffalo herd lived. If one tribe had lost a fight with another, the men in the losing tribe sometimes went on a raid to get revenge.

The bravest thing that a Plains Indian man could do in warfare was to go into an enemy camp at night and take horses from the picket lines. It took a clever, skillful

man to get past the guards who were watching the camp
and to untie the horses and lead them away without rous-
ing anybody.

It was considered almost equally brave to ride up to
an enemy and touch him with your bare hand, or to strike
him with a riding crop or a short stick. A man had to control his horse perfectly, and be a very fine rider, to do this.

Because it took so much courage and cunning to do
these two things, men kept score of the number of times
that they had been successful. If a man had a high score,
he was allowed to wear a war bonnet. This was the same
as being given a medal in our army. Because a man had
to earn the right to wear it by being very brave, the Plains
Indians looked on a war bonnet as something almost sacred. That is why, today, these Indians look down
on white people, or on members of other tribes, who put
on war bonnets and wear them just to show off. The
Plains Indians know these people have not earned the
right to wear Indian medals.

A Plains Indian boy did a very important thing, reli-
giously, when he was about fourteen. He went out all
alone, to look for a spirit guardian who would help and
protect him for the rest of his life. The boy went to a high
bluff or mesa that was not too far from camp. There he

stayed, all alone, for four days and nights. During that whole time, the boy was not supposed to eat or drink, but to pray and wait for the spirit to come to him.

Many boys never saw the vision of a spirit guardian. Those who did not sometimes went again to look for one. Some of them gave up after the first attempt. The boys who had visions usually saw the spirits of animals, such as bears or eagles or coyotes. The animal that the boy saw gave him its own strengths and skills, and told him what he must and must not do to keep them.

A boy who had an eagle vision, for instance, was supposed to see his enemies from afar and to strike them swiftly. He must never eat eagle meat, though, or he would lose his power. At the same time, he was supposed to wear eagle feathers, so he could get extra power directly from them, whenever he needed it.

In some tribes, the boys took names that referred to their spirit guardians. A boy with an eagle guardian might call himself Strong Flier or Long Claws, or some other name that spoke of things that the eagle did.

Because these spirit visions were considered very sacred, the boys told them to no one, but kept their visions secret in their own hearts. Only very old men ever told about their visions. Then, if they wanted to share

the powers given them by their spirit guardians, they told
their visions to their sons or grandsons.

As the girls grew up, they were taught the ways of a
woman's life. They helped their mothers in the teepees.
They learned to cook and sew; to put the teepees up and
to take them down again; to load and unload the pack
horses that carried the household goods. The girls who
were interested in such work learned to paint designs on
clothing and on the rawhide cases in which they kept
their belongings. The girls were taught all the things
that a woman needed to know in order to take care of her
family.

The girls did not join any societies or go out on war
parties. Their mothers kept them close at home, and
watched over them. They did go out with the older women
to help with the skinning and butchering after buffalo
hunts. Girls did not go out to look for visions. The only
religious thing they were taught to do was to take part in
some of the sacred dances.

Still the girls had a good time. Usually three or four
of them worked and sewed together, with an older woman
sitting near them to show them how to do things. The girls
talked things over in groups. They played kickball,
bouncing the rawhide balls with their feet; and stick-

game, which is a game like parcheesi. The young women, too, enjoyed these games, and played them even after they were nearly grown up.

It was not until a young man had been on several hunts and had made his first raid, so he had proved that he could bring home buffalo and horses, that he began to think about getting married. Then he knew that he could take care of himself and of a family, too. Usually he thought things over for a long time, before he made up his mind what girl he wanted to marry.

Then the young man went to his father and told him about it. If the father thought that it was all right, and that his son was old enough and wise enough to make his own home, he agreed. He gave his consent to his son's marrying.

A few days later, the boy's parents put on their best clothes and went to see the family of the girl their son had chosen. To show their respect for the girl and her people, the boy's parents took presents with them: horses, and tanned hides, and knives, and perhaps cloth that they had bought from the white traders. They did not mention their presents; they just tied the horses, loaded with the goods, outside the teepee door. Then the boy's family went inside and sat down and talked to the girl's parents. They said that their son wished to marry the other family's daughter.

When the young man's family had explained things and had gone home, the girl's parents told her about what had happened. Since she was sitting inside the teepee all the time, she naturally knew about it, but her family thought it was polite to tell her, anyway. The girl did not have to marry the young man if she did not want to. She could explain how she felt to her parents. Then they took the horses and the rest of the presents back to the young man's parents.

But if the young woman were pleased, and said so, her family kept the gifts. Then the girl's parents began getting things ready to take to the young man's family. They chose the best things they owned to give away. When ev-

A Marriage Proposal

erything had been gathered together and loaded on horseback, the girl dressed in her best clothes. Then, with her
family following her, she led the horses over to the young
man's teepee. His mother and sisters came out to meet
the bride, and take the horses she was leading. Then the
boy's relatives led the bride inside their teepee, and from
that time on she was a member of that family as well as
of her own.

Making the first teepee for her new home was the most
exciting thing for a young woman; as exciting as the first
buffalo hunt was for a young man.

All the older women gathered at the teepee of
the girl's mother. A woman who was a skilled cutter cut
the buffalo hides into just the right pieces with her knife.

Then all of the women worked to sew the pieces of skin together and make the teepee cover.

After that was finished, the older women gave the bride her presents. Because the teepee and all of the things that went with it belonged to the woman of the family, they gave her woman's things: teepee poles, and gourd dippers, and buckets. They gave her willow-rod beds, with hides for bed coverings, and painted rawhide cases to hold food and clothes that she wanted to store away. Some of these things, such as the teepee poles, a woman kept and used as long as she lived.

As the people grew older and their own families grew up, they spent more time at home. The older men still went hunting, but they did not go out on as many war raids as the younger ones. The older men gave good advice to the young ones; they told them what to do, and the best ways of doing these things. The old men joined separate societies of their own, and spent much of their time meeting together. Then they made plans for the hunts, and for moving camp. They became counselors rather than doers.

The older people were very much respected by the younger Plains Indians for their wisdom and good advice. Because the life of all the people was hard, and not many persons lived to be very old, the younger people took great care of those who had lived a long time. The old people were waited on by their children and grandchildren. What they said was listened to and obeyed. They, in turn, gave much thought and help to the problems of the younger ones.

When the time came for a man to die, he was greatly mourned by his family and friends. Perhaps his wife and children grieved for him so much that they gashed the skin of their arms and legs till the blood ran. Women often cut off their hair when they were in mourning for a loved one.

For a year the whole family painted their faces with ashes instead of with earth colors. They wore old, ragged clothes. They burned or buried everything that had belonged to the dead person, and gave away all their own possessions.

So that they might show their respect for a dead person, his family never spoke his name again. Instead they spoke of his relationship to someone else, saying, "My father," or, "Your brother," or "Snow Woman's husband." They tried to forget his name for all the rest of their lives.

5

HOW THE TRIBES GOVERNED
THEMSELVES

WHEN THE INDIANS first went out on the plains, as we
know, they were in families and little bands. These
groups soon spread wide apart so there would be game
enough for everyone. As time went on, and the people
married and had children, the little bands grew and in-
creased. In time they became nations, and were known
as tribes.

Because the tribes were spread out over so much terri-
tory, each one of them came to have its own ways of doing
things. They became a little different from one another;
first in one way, then in many ways. Even the words that
they spoke became different. We do not know what
languages the Indians spoke when they first crossed the
land bridge from Siberia. We do not even know whether
they all spoke one language; or whether there were many

tongues known among them then. We do know that as
they lived apart from one another each of the tribes developed its own language, and that when the white people first met them, each Indian tribe spoke a little differently from all the others.

That was all right as long as the Indians were camping
along the edges of the plains. They saw few people who
did not belong to their own tribes. As soon as the Indians
got horses and began moving over the grasslands,
though, matters changed. Men from one tribe met those
from others, and when they did, they stopped to talk.

Because their languages were different, they could not
understand one another, so the men began making signs
with their hands to explain what they were trying to say.
As time went on, each tribe learned to make the
same signs that all the others did, to represent certain
thoughts. In this way, what was called "sign language"
was developed. Sign language became so important to
the Plains Indians that after a while people even used
it in speaking to members of their own tribes. They
would talk along in words, saying the same things with
gestures, and not realize that they were using their hands
at all.

Since each tribe had its own customs, and since they
were so scattered over the land, each one governed itself

GREETING!   GIVE ME   WATER TO DRINK

OVER THERE   A CHEYENNE (MAKE SAWING MOTION)   IS COMING ALONG

ON HORSEBACK   IT IS RAINING   SUN IS SHINING

BRAVE   BAD, OR MEAN   THE END

SIGN   LANGUAGE

in its own way. The Indians did not sit down to plan their governments and write their constitutions, or hold conventions, the way the white people do. The Indians worked out their own rules and passed them on by word of mouth. In that way everybody finally learned to know and obey the regulations. The people knew they had to obey, because staying alive depended on staying a member of the tribe.

Every tribe had a special group of men who were its advisers and counselors. They were not elected to do this work, but were chosen because they were older men who were known to be good and wise. Just because each person separately went to them for help and wisdom, all the people together did the same thing.

Of the counselors, there was always one who was thought to be wiser and to have more knowledge than anyone else in his tribe. He came to be thought of as the chief counselor or what we call the chief. The chief was not a governor or a king. He could not hand on his office to his sons any more than he could give them his wisdom and experience. He could not force the people to obey him. Still, in time, a chief became the one man in each tribe who made final decisions about important things during peace time.

Since the counselors and their chief were too old to take active part in fighting, they did not have much to do with governing their tribes during war times. Then the younger men took over, and the responsibility for caring for the people was in their hands. If the tribe were attacked, one of the men who had fought bravely in other battles became the war chief. He was not elected to his office any more than the peace chief was, but he was recognized as the leader of the tribe during the war.

If the tribe were attacking, the plan that was used was a different one. Then a man decided to go against an enemy tribe to get horses or goods, or to prove his own bravery. He called all the other men together, and told them what he wanted to do. Those who wished to might join him. If they did join, the first man went as the leader. The responsibility for the lives of the men who followed him was in his hands. That meant that the leader not only had to be brave, but also wise and skillful, so that his followers would not be in danger of being killed or hurt. When the fighting was over, the war chief was no longer head of the tribe. He was just another one of the fighting men.

Besides the chiefs and counselors, there was another group who took part in governing the tribe. These were the members of the men's societies. Sometimes, as in the buffalo hunts, the members of the societies served as game wardens. Sometimes, when the tribe was encamped and there was no hunting going on, the societies acted as camp police. Sometimes, when there was important news to be told to the people, they were the announcers.

Each society in the tribe took its turn at these duties. Sometimes it was the Kit Foxes, sometimes the Gourd Rattle Dancers, sometimes the Black-Painted Legs, or sometimes the Crazy Dogs who did the work. Usually the societies alternated, and each one knew when its turn came to serve. If one of the societies were known to be especially good at a certain kind of work, and that was the work that had to be done, then the other societies would ask that one to take charge out of turn.

In camp, it was the duty of the police to see that the teepees were pitched right, and that all the ropes and poles were firm and tight. The police instructed the people to keep their camps clean and neat, with all the rubbish picked up and burned. They told the men where to pasture their horses during the day, and where to tie the horses on the picket lines at night. It was part of the police work to see that people did not get into fights

A Member of the Crazy Dog Society with His Attendant

or quarrels with one another, and that there was no stealing. In fact, the Indian police did just the same kinds of work that our police do.

When the men went hunting, the society members were the game wardens. They kept all the men riding together, so that no one could charge ahead of the other hunters and scare off the game before everybody had had a chance to shoot. The wardens gave the signal to charge at the herd and start shooting. They told the women where to stand and how long to wait before they came up to skin the buffalo.

It was important for the Plains Indians not to kill off too much game, or to kill the buffalo cows and calves, in order to keep the herds large and growing. In that way there would always be enough meat for everybody's needs. These were the reasons it was important to have game wardens on duty in the big hunts. The wardens were so busy taking care of the herds that they had no time to get meat for their own families. The hunters shared their meat with the wardens.

When the societies were acting as camp announcers, their most important work was to tell the people when the camp was going to be moved. Then the society members rode through the camp, calling out when the tribe was going to leave; and how far they were going to travel. In that way everybody could know what the peace chief and counselors were planning for the tribe.

If a family, or one of the societies, were planning to have a great feast; or if a member of a society were going to get married; or if there were a religious ceremony to be held, the announcers told about these things, too. The same announcers told the whole camp when a man was planning to lead out a war party.

Sometimes a family would decide to have a give-away. This was like the giving away that came after a funeral, or after a boy's first hunt; but it was given for a different reason. Many times give-aways were like our birthday parties or holiday celebrations. They were given in honor of a child, or of a young man or woman.

The difference between our birthday parties and an Indian give-away is that at a give-away, instead of geting presents, the one who was holding the celebration gave gifts to other people. A family took the best things that its members had, and sometimes everything that they had, and gave the things away to people who were in need. It was very important not to give away to your own relatives, or to people who owned plenty of things of their own. One reason for having give-aways was to teach the young people to take care of those who were less fortunate than themselves, and to be generous and kind to everybody in the tribe.

Many times a family gave away all its possessions at one give-away. When they had done that, the family started in again to build up their goods. The members of the family knew that because they had shown their own generosity, other people would not let them suffer want. If a man were known to have been generous and kind to others during his own youth, he need not fear starvation in his old age. Other people, when they had their give-aways, would remember his generosity. They would take care of him then. This was not really a part of governing the tribe, but it was one of the important rules by which the members of the tribes lived and helped each other.

6

THE SUN DANCE CEREMONY

THE BIGGEST GIVE-AWAYS held by all the Plains Indian tribes came in the middle of the summer, at the time of the Sun Dance ceremony. The Sun Dance was a great religious ceremony, which was held every year. Each of the plains tribes performed the ceremony a little differently from the others, but in some ways all the Sun Dances were pretty much alike. The one we are going to talk about here is the ceremony that was given by the Kiowa Indians, who live in the southern part of the Great Plains.

Long before the time for the ceremony came, a place to put the big camp for the dance had to be chosen. This decision was made by the man who was the religious chief of the tribe for that one dance. During the Sun Dance time, this man governed the whole tribe. It was as if one

143

of our ministers were asked, during the Christmas
season, or Easter week, to act as mayor of his city.

The Sun Dance chief made all the plans long ahead
of time. He picked out a place where there would be
plenty of wood for fires. There had to be lots of grass for
the horses, and he made sure that there was a lot of water
for everybody. Then on a certain day that he selected,
the Sun Dance chief called all of the young men whom
he could together. They rode out to visit all the families
in the tribe, to give them word when and where the Sun
Dance was to be held.

Sometimes this was a long trip. Many of the families
camped away from the others, where the hunting and
grazing were good. All of the families had to be notified.
It might take several days to get word to all of them. But
no matter how long the trip took, the Sun Dance chief
and the young men who were with him rode slowly. The
Plains Indians thought that you should never hurry
about sacred things.

When all of the families in the tribe had been notified
about the Sun Dance, they began to come to the camping
place that had been chosen for it. The people pitched
their teepees there. In other camps, the teepees were all

set in a straight line facing east. For the Sun Dances the people camped in a big circle, with their teepees facing towards the center. A cleared place was left in the middle of the circle. There a special shelter, called the Sun Dance lodge, was to be built.

It usually took four days and nights for the whole tribe to gather together. The people felt that this length of time was just right, because in the Sun Dance everything was done by fours. The next four days, after all the tribe had met, were called "the getting-ready four days."

First, the center pole had to be cut for the lodge. Cutting the poles was a ceremonial thing that only a woman could do, and it was believed that cutting it was so sacred an act that it was dangerous. So the woman who cut the center pole was usually a captive from another tribe. The tribe did not want one of their own women to be in danger. The captive woman was dressed in her best clothes. Her face was painted yellow. She rode out of camp just behind the Sun Dance chief, on a fine horse. Behind them rode all the young men of the tribe.

When the riders came within sight of the tree that had been chosen for the center pole, the Sun Dance chief pointed to it with his whole arm. Then the young men rode forward past the chief and the captive woman, and charged at the tree as if it were an enemy. Striking the tree counted the same as striking an enemy, and the first four men to touch the center pole could count the blow as if it were a war honor.

After the young men struck the tree, the captive woman chopped it down. Then she painted four wide red stripes around the lower part of the tree trunk. After that, she took off all her fine clothes and tied them to the fork of the tree, as an offering. When she had stepped aside, in an old, ragged dress that she had been wearing under her good one, all the other people came up and tied their offerings of food or clothes to the fork of the tree. Last of all, the Sun Dance chief tied little painted rawhide images of a man and a buffalo to the tree trunk. This was to show that the dance was given to the sun by men, in gratitude for the buffalo. Then all the men joined in carrying the tree back to the camp. There they ceremoniously set the tree in place in the middle of the camp circle.

The next day all the men went out together to cut logs. The men brought the logs back to camp, and placed them around the center pole. The logs were set in a circle about forty feet across, their lower ends planted in the earth as if they were still growing trees. Each pair of logs was about ten feet apart. The men tied big beams from the center post out to the circle of logs. Then they tied beams from the fork of one upright post to that of the next. All the logs were tied together with rawhide ropes. The ropes bound the whole lodge together, so that it would always stand firm. The men tied their ropes so securely that many years after the last Sun Dance was held, in 1890, the lodge where it had been given was still standing.

On the third of the getting-ready days, all the people of the tribe gathered willow branches to cover the lodge. The green leafy boughs made a shade, so the hot sun would not burn the dancers. Everybody took part in this work: men, and women, and children. The people all wore their finest buckskin clothes, and they rode out into the woods together, singing. This was the one time of the year when a young man and woman who were not married might ride on the same horse. In fact, if a young man asked a girl to ride with him, it was the same as asking her to marry him.

Late in the afternoon of the third day, the people all rode back to camp. They were singing, and they wore wreaths of green willow branches on their heads. The people beat time to their singing with green willow branches which they held in their hands. Behind the horses, and tied to them with ropes, were whole willow trees to be used to cover the lodge. The singing people rode four times around the framework of the lodge.

They did not go inside it. Then the men untied the willow boughs their horses had been dragging, and then the men covered the lodge with the leafy branches. When they did this work, the men were always careful to leave an open doorway on the east side of the lodge.

The fourth of the getting-ready days was called "the Day of Opening the Lodge." In some ways it was the most important day of the whole ceremony. Early in the morning, the word went through the camp, "The Mud Heads are coming!" That was the signal for the women to gather up everything that they owned, and to get all the things safely inside the teepees. If anything were left lying around outside, the Mud Heads had the right to pick it up and throw it away, or to break it or spoil it. The Sun Dance chief chose the men who were to act as clowns and nobody else knew who they were. The Mud Heads coated their bodies with mud, and wore mud-coated buckskin masks to hide their faces. Some of the clowns pretended to be horses, and carried other men on their backs like riders. One Mud Head might pretend to be a woman, with a bundle of rags on his back for a baby. The woman would have a pretend-husband running behind her and whipping her with his ridingwhip.

All the people ran inside their teepees when they saw the Mud Heads coming, for fear that they would be whipped, too. After the Mud Heads had gone by, the people came out and watched them, and had fun seeing what the Mud Heads did to each other.

On the same day, after the Mud Head parade, came the big opening parade for the Dance. All the societies took part in this procession. The men all wore their society dance costumes, like wearing uniforms. With the Sun Dance chief leading them, the societies rode slowly through the camp, and then over to the lodge. When the members of the societies were all gathered inside the lodge, a man rode in with the hide of a newly killed yearling buffalo bull. This man had to go out early in the morning of the Day of Opening the Lodge, and he had to shoot the buffalo with a single arrow, if the dance were to go right. The Sun Dance chief took the hide from the hunter, and tied it with the other offerings, in the fork of the center pole. Then everything was ready for the Sun Dance to begin.

The Sun Dancers were always men. Most of them were young. They danced because they had made promises or vows to do so. Men made the vows because they or their relatives were sick, and they thought that dancing in the Sun Dance was a way to recover health. A man also promised to dance in the Sun Dance because he wanted success in hunting or fighting, or because he wanted health throughout a long life to come. Sometimes a woman made a Sun Dance vow, if she or her children were sick, but she didn't dance herself. Her husband or brother danced for her.

The dancers went into the lodge on the evening of the fourth getting-ready day. With each dancer there went an old man. The old man was the dancer's teacher, and showed him what to do during the ceremony. A man took the same place inside the lodge that his teacher had

had when he first danced. The Sun Dance chief sat in a little, leafy shelter on the west side of the lodge. Behind him there was hung a doll-like image that represented the Sun Dance power.

Now, when the men were all inside the lodge and ready, the dance could begin. The dancers took off all their clothes except their breechclouts and moccasins. The teachers painted each of the dancers with blue and yellow and green paint. Everybody was forbidden to wear red clothes or paint during the Sun Dance.

Then the teachers tied green willow branches to the dancers' heads and wrists and ankles. Each teacher gave the dancer he was helping an eagle wingbone whistle, with white feathers from an eagle's breast tied to it. The dancers stood in a curving line, facing the Sun Dance chief and the doll that hung behind him. The teachers sat in their places around the walls of the lodge. When everybody was in line, the teachers began to drum and sing. The dancers stood still, lifting their feet up and down in time with the singing.

All the dances of the four dancing days were the same as the first one. At the end of every fourth song, the Sun Dance chief took a crow wing feather fan, and with it in his hand he chased the dancers four times around the

The Sun Dance

lodge. Then the dancing men could lie down and rest for a while. They were allowed to rest and sleep, but during the four days of dancing the men were not permitted to eat or drink. Their teachers were not allowed to eat or drink, either.

Sometimes, after a man had starved and thirsted for two or three days, he would be so weak that he would fall down when the Sun Dance chief chased him. Then the man's teacher would help him up, and lead him back to his place by the wall of the lodge. Some men said they saw visions of their spirit guardians or of other spirits when they were unconscious at these times. Other men did not claim to have seen visions. But whether a man had a vision or not, if he went through the whole four days of the Sun Dance without eating or drinking, he knew that his vow was fufilled and that his prayers would be answered.

Every night, after the day's dancing ended at sundown, the dancers stayed in the lodge. They were not allowed to leave it until the end of the ceremony. But during the same time there was feasting and celebration in camp. Families held give-aways. Members of other tribes came and visited, and feasts were given for them. The Sun Dance was like our Christmas, a time of good will and happiness for everybody. All the people felt peaceful and contented. No war parties started out, and other tribes did not attack a Sun Dance camp. It was a time for everybody to feel secure.

After the four days of the Sun Dance, when the Sun Dance chief had chased the dancers around the lodge for the last time, and this time had chased them clear outside the shelter, the camp broke up and the families scattered out again. They went away so as to make the most of the good summer grass, while it was still green and fresh, before the heat had browned and dried it. The people could not stay on where they were, because in eight days the horses had eaten all the grass around the camp, and there was no feed left for them.

Before they left the camping place, the Sun Dance chief called all the people together and blessed them. At the same time, he told them where he thought the Sun Dance would be held in the coming year. He told the people this so that they could begin to gather in towards the place when they felt that the time was about right for them to go there. Then the tribe broke up into bands and families, and the smaller groups spread out over the plains to wait for the next year to come.

7

INDIAN DOCTORS AND MEDICINES

WHENEVER PEOPLE get sick, they wonder about the things that caused the sickness, and try to figure out what those things were. This is so they can avoid them in the future, and not get sick in the same way another time. Nowadays we know that most sicknesses are caused by microbes, but there was a time when our great-grandparents thought that bad dreams or night air could make you sick. That was before our doctors had discovered that there were such things as microbes.

Like our own ancestors, the Plains Indians had never heard about microbes or about the diseases that microbes cause. They had never heard about hospitals or scientific laboratories or penicillin or vaccinations. But the Plains Indians did believe in spirits, and they thought and talked about the spirits a great deal. So it was that they came to believe that evil spirits caused diseases.

The bad spirits were supposed to make people sick by shooting them with magic weapons, like stones or cactus thorns, or with little sharp teeth of wild animals. When a person became ill, it was believed that one of the magic weapons had been shot into his body by a spell. The way to make the sick person well, the Indians believed, was to remove the magic weapon.

The Indians did not think that everybody knew how to get it out. To heal sick people, they believed, a man had to be so good himself that all the good spirits were on his side, fighting with him. Then he was strong enough to drive out the evil spirits, and he could be a doctor. We feel a good deal the same way about our doctors, and we expect them to be good men, always.

The Indian doctor, when he was called on to heal somebody, came and sat beside the sick person and asked him many questions, just as our doctors do. He needed to know where the patient's pain was, and if it were a steady pain, or one that came and went. The doctor wanted to know everything that the patient had been doing before he felt sick; where he had been; whom he had seen; and what he had said to people or they had said to him. This was to make sure that the evil spirit had come into the sick person's body from outside, and had not been put there by something wrong that he him-self had done or said.

When the doctor had found out everything that he could by asking questions, he went to work to treat the patient. All of the doctors sang songs and rattled gourds, and some of the doctors danced. This was so that the evil spirits would know that the good spirits were coming to fight them, and to encourage the good spirits to fight hard.

When the doctor believed that he had sung and had shaken his rattle long enough, according to the rules that his spirit guardian had given him; he took a small stone knife and cut an "X" on the patient's skin, over the place where the pain was worst. The doctor sucked at the cut as quickly and lightly as he could. After four tries, the doctor would pretend to suck out the magic weapon that had made the patient sick. The doctor would hold the weapon up in his hand, and show it to everybody in the sick person's family. Then the doctor would throw the weapon in the fire, so that the evil spirits couldn't get it back and use it again to hurt somebody else. This was the magical part of the treatment.

Not all of the curing was magical, though. After the Indian doctor had taken out the magic weapon, he would

An Indian Doctor

tell his patient to lie quiet and to rest; to eat light food
and not too much of it, just as our doctors tell us to do
when we are sick. Often the Indian doctor would give
the family special instructions about bathing the patient.
He would give them herbs to make into teas for the patient to drink. Some of these herbs, such as peyote cactus
and wild sage and mint, were so good for certain diseases
that we still use them today. The rules were all like those
our doctors make for their patients to follow.

The Plains Indians did not believe that people who
were hurt in accidents, or men who were injured in fighting, had been hurt by evil spirits. Everybody knew that
if a man fell off his horse and broke his leg, he wouldn't
be able to walk or ride for a while. Nobody believed that
an evil spirit had got into the horse to make the rider fall.
It was just an accident that had happened.

When there was an accident, or when a man had been
hurt in fighting, there were special doctors in some tribes,
who were called on to take care of the person who had
been hurt. These men were called Buffalo Doctors. They
wore headdresses made out of the scalps of buffalo bulls;
and they stamped their feet and roared like buffaloes
when they danced. Besides dancing and singing, the
Buffalo Doctors did other things to help their patients.

A Healing Ceremony

We call some of the things that they did first aid, and we think that everybody should know about them.

The most important thing that the Buffalo Doctors did was to keep everything near the injury as clean as possible. They washed cuts with hot water, and bandaged them with strips of soft, clean deer hide. Sometimes the Buffalo Doctor would put a dressing of warm, clean fat over a cut, to keep the dirt out of it. If an arm or a leg were broken, the Buffalo Doctor put on splints that were as good as any that we know about today. The splints were made out of stiff, hard pieces of rawhide, and tied in place with strips of soft-tanned skin. The Buffalo Doctors even knew how long to leave the splints on the injuries, so the bones would knit right and the arm or leg would be well again.

Because they lived outdoors and their life was active; and because they ate plain foods and few sweets, the Plains Indians were generally healthy people.

Until the white people came on the plains, in about 1850, the Indians there had never had mumps or measles or smallpox. They had never had colds or pneumonia or tuberculosis. These were all diseases that the white people brought with them from Europe, and that the Indians caught from them. Because the Indians had never had these sicknesses before, their bodies were not able to resist the diseases, and many of the Indians died suddenly in a short time. European diseases still make Indians sicker than they do white people. Getting new sicknesses in this way has been one of the worst things that have happened to the Plains Indians. Their doctors did not know how to treat these new diseases, or get rid of the microbes that caused them.

8

A PLAINS INDIAN COOKBOOK

SINCE THE Plains Indians could not read or write their languages, they never put their knowledge down on paper. Everything that they knew they had to remember from word-of-mouth teaching. Cooking was remembered and taught in the same way that other subjects were.

Because a girl had to know and remember everything about foods, she started learning about them when she was very small. First, she went with her mother and the other women to gather fruits and berries. Later, when she was older, she went with the women who followed the hunters to skin and butcher the game. When the meat had been brought back to the teepee, the girl learned to preserve it for winter use.

By the time that a girl was ready to marry, she had learned to be a good cook, and to take care of everything that she used in preparing food. She learned to keep all her kitchen tools clean and ready to use. If a girl did not know these things, and if she were not careful about doing them, people did not think that she was ready to marry.

Although the Plains Indians ate more meat than any other food, they knew about and used many roots, berries, and other plants that grew in their country. The Indians had no cows or goats, and nobody was ever able to tame the buffalo, so the Indians lacked milk, butter and cheese. They had no chickens, but they ate the eggs of wild birds, when they found nests. In most ways the food that the Plains Indians ate was good, even though it was different from ours.

The most important meat to the Plains Indians was that of the buffalo. There were many different ways of cooking this meat. The easiest way was to put a slice of the meat on a green stick, and hold it or hang it over the fire. Meat cooked like this was half broiled, half roasted, and it tasted very good. When a woman wanted extra seasoning for her meat, she made the broiling fire of pecan or hickory wood. The wood smoke flavored the buffalo meat, just as it does our ham or bacon.

If she had plenty of time, and if the meat were tough, the woman boiled it. The most famous way was by means

of stone-boiling. To cook meat by this method, the
woman first dug a hole in the ground with a sharp-
pointed stick. She lined the hole with a clean, freshly
scraped hide, and weighted the edges of the skin down
with big stones. Then the woman filled the hide with water and chunks of meat. Next, the cook built a fire on top
of a pile of clean stones. She was careful to select small,
round stones, of a kind that would not explode if they
got too hot. When the fire had heated the stones red hot,
the woman lifted them from the fire on forked green
sticks. She dropped the hot stones into the hideful of
meat, being careful not to let the food splash over the
edges of the hole onto the ground. As the hot stones were
put into the stew, the water and meat were heated until
they began to boil. It took a long time to cook a meal in
this way, because as the stones cooled they had to be

taken out of the stew and reheated in the fire. But the Plains Indians liked their meat better when it was cooked in this way than when it was prepared by any other method.

Another famous way of preparing meat was as pemmican. To make this dish, the woman sliced buffalo or deer meat so that it was as thin as paper. Then she hung the meat over racks that she had built of poles, and she set the racks outside her teepee, so the sun could dry and cook the meat. The woman brought her meat indoors at night, so the damp night air would not spoil it. After about four days of sunning, the meat was so dry that it was brittle. It tasted a little like our dried smoked beef. Sometimes meat was stored as soon as it was dried, without any other preparation.

If she wanted to make pemmican, though, the woman took her dried meat and put it in a wooden bowl, or on a stiff, dry hide. Then she pounded and pounded the meat with a stone hammer, until the beef was powdered fine. Next, if the woman had berries or fruits that she had dried, she added them to the pounded meat, and pounded

FLINT BLADE

GROOVED STONE HAMMER

and mixed all the foods together. After that, the woman put the mixture in flat rawhide cases. She sealed the cases by pouring clean melted fat over their openings, and letting the fat harden like paraffin.

Pemmican tasted better than it sounds. In winter, a woman cooked her pemmican just as she did fresh meat, by boiling it with stones. After the Indians got kettles from the white traders, they could cook meat and pemmican in kettles hung over the fires. Pemmican soaked up lots of water, and it took a long time to cook, but when it was done, it made a good stew for cold days. Men on war parties, or children who were playing away from home, carried handfuls of pemmican with them to eat raw. Nobody liked pemmican raw as well as they did when it was cooked, but it was just as nourishing and good for them raw as when it had been made into stew. Pemmican was a sort of Indian K-ration, that could be eaten in any way that was convenient.

When the man of the family had killed a big buffalo, his wife made sausage out of the marrow. She broke up the big leg bones with her hammer, and boiled the pieces of bone to get out all the marrow fat. Then she put the fat into pieces of cleaned intestine, and hung the filled cases up to dry in the sun until she needed the sausage. If she had herbs, like wild sage or wild onions, she added them to the marrow, as seasoning.

Deer meat, or venison, was cooked in the same ways as buffalo beef. So was antelope meat, if a tribe went far enough west to hunt this game. Some Plains Indian tribes ate rabbits, prairie dogs, squirrels, and other small rodents, but most of the Plains Indians did not care for them. The plains peoples very seldom ate fish or water-fowl. They were afraid of things that grew and lived near the water, for large rivers and lakes were not common in the plains country. All of the peoples of the plains ate some game birds, like wild turkeys, quail, and prairie hens. These were all native American birds.

The Plains Indians used salt to season their meat dishes. The salt came from salt beds, where it was on the surface of the ground, or from salt springs, where it was dissolved in the water. When the salt was dry, the Indians dissolved it in water, and then boiled it until the water had evaporated, to be sure it would be clean. A deposit of salt was left on the hide or kettle where the water had been boiled. The woman scraped up the dried salt, pounded it fine, and then put it away in little buckskin bags to use when she needed it. This salt was grayish in color, and rather coarse in texture, but it was better than no salt at all. Water from the salt springs was also boiled, and the salt it had contained was saved in the same way. Sometimes, if a woman had used up all her salt, she might use finely powdered pecan or hickory ashes to season her meat.

Many fruits grew wild on the plains, in summer. There were wild currants and blackberries, wild strawberries and buffalo berries and skunk berries. Later in the season came the wild cherries and the chokecherries; and the sand plums and the tree plums.

The women and girls spent days at a time gathering these fruits and berries. As they picked the fruit, they put it in rawhide bags, since they had no baskets. Late in the fall, the women went out to gather wild grapes from the vines that grew along the creek banks.

The Plains Indians ate some of the wild fruit fresh, as soon as it was gathered. Much of the fruit, though, the women saved for winter. They pounded the fruit first with their stone hammers. Then they made the pounded pulp into cakes which they laid out on clean rawhides to dry in the sun. The cakes of fruit were mixed with dried meat to make pemmican, or were sealed into rawhide cases and stored away, as the pemmican was.

There were wild vegetables, too, to be picked during the spring and summer months. There were lambs' quarters, and poke shoots, and wild spinach. There were wild potatoes, too, and jerusalem artichokes, which grew underground like the potatoes. Some trees and bushes have green sprouts that are good to eat in the spring, and the Indians knew about these and gathered them. A few of the wild vegetables, like potatoes and artichokes which they knew would keep, the women dried and saved as they did fruits.

Because they raised no crops or gardens, the Plains Indians had no grain to make bread. When they were near tribes that grew corn, the Plains Indians traded dried meat or tanned hides for cornmeal, and then they could make mush or hoecakes. Sometimes the Pueblo Indians from New Mexico came east to visit the plains tribes, and they traded the kind of thin cornbread that they call tortillas for hides or meat. After the white people came, the Plains Indians could get flour and meal from them, and then they learned to make bread for themselves.

The tribes who lived in the southwestern part of the plains country also made a meal out of mesquite beans.

MESQUITE

The beans are very hard when they are dry, and it takes a lot of pounding to crack their shells and get out the kernels. Grinding the beans between two stones is hard work, too. Once the kernels have been ground, they make a fine, light-yellow meal, that looks a little like cornmeal, and seems to have almost no taste. Mesquite meal is one of the strongest foods in the world, though. A pinch of it stirred into a cup of water will give you enough energy to work on all day, if you drink it at breakfast time. Mesquite meal can be eaten dry, too, but, like any other meal, it is choky when it is taken that way. Men who went out on hunting parties or war raids always took mesquite meal with them. As long as they had the meal they could keep traveling without stopping to cook when they got hungry. All they had to do was swallow a little of this food.

For dessert, the Plains Indians ate fresh or dried fruits. When they found a hive of wild bees, the Indians took the honey. In later years, the plains people got sugar and candy from the white traders. The older people didn't like the taste of the sugar or of the things that were made from it, because they were too sweet. So it happened that the little children were the first Indians who learned to eat and like candy.

There were other Plains Indians recipes, besides those that are listed here. These are the most common ones. They are the recipes that every woman knew, to make the dishes that every family liked to eat. All the Plains Indian women were proud of being good cooks and of keeping their families well-fed. In the same way, the men were proud of being good hunters, and of bringing in plenty of game to be cooked for their families.

9

HOW THE PLAINS INDIANS MADE THINGS

ALMOST ALL of the things that the Plains Indians made and used began with buffalo or deer hides. This was for two reasons. The first was that since the people were moving around all the time, they did not want to have things that would be heavy to carry with them. The second reason was that the Plains Indians killed many buffalo and deer for food, so they had plenty of hides to use in making things.

There are two main ways of preparing hides for use. The first is by sun-drying, to make rawhide. The second is by rubbing and treating, or tanning, to make soft skin. Each way is important for making special things. The way a skin is to be used determines the way it is prepared.

Making rawhide, of course, was the easier way of treating the skins. When she made rawhide, a Plains Indian woman first fastened the skin she was using flat

on the ground. She drove wooden pegs through the edges
of the hide and down into the earth. When the skin was
spread flat and fastened firmly, the woman took an elbow-
shaped tool, with a bone or antler handle and a sharp
stone or steel blade, and scraped every bit of meat off
the hide. Then the woman turned the hide over, and

HIDE SCRAPER
STEEL BLADE, BONE
HANDLE- DOTS MEAN NO. OF
YEARS USED

HIDE SCRAPER: STONE BLADE ON BONE HANDLE

again fastened it to the ground. Still using her elbow-
shaped tool, she scraped all the hair from the outer
surface of the hide. After that, the woman left the hide to
dry in the sun for three or four days, and then it was ready
to use.

Dry rawhide is nearly as hard as a piece of wood. It is
difficult to cut or to work with it in any way. But if rawhide has been made right, it will last a long time, and it is
good for making many things that get hard use.

Soft-tanning the hides was slower and harder **work**

than making rawhide. To soft-tan a hide, the woman stretched it and scraped it as if she were going to make rawhide. After the skin was clean, the woman took the liver and brains of the animal with whose skin she was working, and cooked them with some fat. Then she pounded the meat and fat into a paste. It was a Plains Indian saying that every hide had brains enough to tan itself. After her paste was ready, the woman rubbed it into the flesh side of the hide with a flat stone. It took a lot of rubbing to get all the paste worked into the hide, but the woman had to work without stopping, until the mixture was thoroughly rubbed into the hide. If she stopped too soon, the hide got stiff. Then she had to work it over again, with fresh paste, or use it for rawhide.

When all the paste was rubbed into the skin, the woman sprinkled the hide all over with warm water. She rolled the skin up tightly. Then she put it in a shady place, where it would not get too warm, and left it there for a few days. The skin soaked up every bit of the paste during this time.

Next the woman unrolled the hide. She began rubbing the skin back and forth with her hands, pulling and stretching it, and working with the skin to soften it. This work, too, took her a long time. A woman might have to

Preparing a Hide for Tanning

work for a whole day to get a big skin soft. And while she was doing this part of the work, too, the woman could not stop except for a few minutes at a time, to eat and rest. If she let the skin dry out, even a little, she had to start all over again. When a hide had been soft-tanned in the right way, it was as soft as cloth, and just as easy to cut. The soft skin was a creamy white color. A soft-tanned hide was not waterproof, so if it got wet it would harden and stiffen, and would have to be worked all over again.

Soft-tanned hides could be made waterproof by smoking them. Many different plants were used to make the smoke. Some tribes used cedar or juniper branches or roots. Others used fungus growths from the roots or trunks of trees, while still others used wild grasses or weeds.

The most important thing was to make a fire that gave

very little flame and a lot of smoke. When the fire was smouldering, a frame of sticks, like the frame of the tee-pee, was built over it. Then the hide was stretched and tied over the sticks, and was left to smoke for several hours. The woman watched the hide closely, to be sure that the fire did not go out, or that the skin did not get too dry and start to burn.

After a skin had been smoked, it was hung up outside the teepee to air for a while, before it was used. Smoked hides, even those many years old, usually smell a little of the smoke. The smoked skins are golden-brown in color, and are even softer to touch than are the white soft-tanned skins. When people speak of "buckskin color," they are usually thinking of the color of a smoked hide.

Rawhide was used to make moccasin soles; for the cases that held clothing or dried foods; and for ropes and saddles. These, and other articles that were made of raw-hide, were things that got hard use, and had to be made of a material that would wear well.

Soft-tanned hides were used to make the moccasin uppers; and for dresses, shirts, leggings, teepees, and bedding. Hides were soft-tanned to make winter wraps, but the hair was left on them so that they would be extra warm. Smoked hides were often used for making moccasin uppers, or for clothing to be worn in wet weather.

The thread that was used for sewing all of these things was made of sinew from a deer or buffalo. The sinew of the animal that can be used for thread is the large, heavy muscle that lies along either side of the backbone. These muscles can be cut out of the meat in long, flat strips. After the meat scraps have been scraped away and the sinews have been dried, the muscle fibres can be separated from one another into long, fine threads. If the sinew thread is moistened a little when it is used, the natural glue that is found in all animal fibers will cause the threads to stick to each other, and to the skins that are being sewn together. This makes sinew thread the best to use in sewing moccasins or clothes that are made of leather.

Because they had no needles, the Plains Indian women made awls, or thrusting points, to sew with. At first the women used finely pointed pieces of bone or stone, but after the white traders brought them metal, in about 1850, the women had steel awls. In sewing with an awl, a woman made holes in the skin, one at a time, and then threaded the sinew through the holes. This was a slower way of sewing than with a needle, but the sinew could be pulled tight and the work made very firm.

In most of the Plains tribes, both the men and the women were saddle makers. The saddle frames were made of forked tree limbs, or of buffalo rib bones, or of elk antlers. The pieces of the frame were tied together with wet rawhide ropes. Rawhide, when it is wet, will stick to things just the same way that sinew does, so the process was like tying and gluing the pieces at the same time.

PAIR OF ANTLERS
PAIR OF BOARDS

RAWHIDE COVERED SADDLE
HOLES ARE FOR TYING
EQUIPMENT TO SADDLE

After the ropes that held the frame together were thoroughly dry, the saddle cover was put over the frame. This was done by soaking a large piece of rawhide in water, and then cutting it into the right shape. Then the cover was sewn over the frame with wet rawhide strings. When the cover had dried and set, the saddle was as solid as if it had a metal frame.

The halters that went on the horses' heads were made of rawhide ropes or of braided strips of soft-tanned hide.

A Cheyenne Silver Bridle

Sometimes the halters were trimmed with metal orna-
ments or with beadwork.

The Plains Indians usually rode without stirrups.
Some men did not even tie their saddles to their horses'
backs, but held them in place by balancing and gripping
them with their knees. Pack saddles, to hold the drag
loads or the light loads that were tied on the horses'
backs, were made in the same way as the riding saddles.
Usually, the pack saddles were made with higher pom-
mels and horns than were the riding saddles.

The rawhide cases which the Plains Indians used to
hold their food and clothing were shaped rather like
envelopes. To make a case, a hide was laid out flat on the
ground. The shape of the case was marked out with a
knife point, and then the hide was cut into shape. The
places where the folds of the envelope were to be were
pressed down with the blunt edge of the knife, so the hide
would bend easily along the lines. Holes were cut in the

ends of the envelope flaps, and soft hide strings were passed through the holes.

When one of these cases was to be packed, it was laid out flat. Then the articles it would hold were laid out on top of the case. Then the side flaps were turned up over the contents and were tied together. Last of all, the end flaps were tied on the outside of the case. An envelope made and packed like this would hold many things, but still it was flat and easy to carry. The cases are often called "parfleches," which is a French name for anything made of rawhide.

Rawhide ropes were used for a great many purposes. Usually, when a woman wanted to make a rope, she first soaked the rawhide in water, to make it pliable and easy to work. Then the skin was cut into one long strip with a knife. To cut the hide, the woman began at the outer edge and went around and round the skin, pulling the strip of hide out straight and flat as she cut it. If the cutting were done in the right way, a whole skin made one flat, even string. This big cord could then be divided into shorter lengths, to be used as they were needed.

Usually four strips of rawhide were braided together to make a rope. If the rope were to be extra strong, six or eight strips of skin were used. If only a light cord were needed, two pieces of rawhide were twisted together by rolling them between the palms of the woman's hand, or over her knee. All the time that the hide was being braided or twisted, the woman kept it wet. Afterwards, she coiled the rope, and let it dry out very slowly, so it would not get hard or brittle. Last of all she rubbed the rope with fat to keep it pliable. Some ropes made by Plains Indian workers have lasted as long as a hundred years, and they are still strong and supple enough to use today.

Both rawhide and soft-tanned skins were used in making a pair of moccasins. Moccasin making was the work that the Indian women had to do most often. Moccasins are light shoes, so they wear out quickly. A Plains Indian woman always had her sewing bag with her. In it she had moccasins cut out and ready to make up for the different members of her family.

To make a pair of moccasins, the woman first asked the person who was going to wear them to stand flat on a piece of rawhide. Then the woman took a stick of charcoal from the fire, and drew the outlines of the wearer's feet on the hide. After she had done this, she cut the footprints out of the hide with her knife, and the moccasin soles were ready to be used.

Next, the woman took a piece of soft-tanned hide, and

cut out the upper parts of the moccasins, measuring them against the soles to be sure that they would fit smoothly. Then she cut a narrow strip of soft hide, to sew between the sole and upper of each moccasin. A strip like this is called a welt, and it acts as a pad for the sole of the moccasin, and makes the shoe wear better. Welts are used in fitting our shoe soles today.

When the woman had all the different parts of the moccasins cut out, she was ready to begin sewing. She punched holes through the upper, the welt, and the sole with her awl, and then put her sinew thread through the holes. The woman used an over-and-over sewing stitch, like the stitch that we use in making a hem in a dress or skirt. The woman was always careful not to tie knots in her sinew thread, because the knots might rub the wearer's feet, and make sore places,

The woman began sewing at the toe of the moccasin, and worked around the outside of the sole to the heel. Then she broke off her thread, and began sewing again, this time making the seam along the instep of the foot. In this way the uppers and soles were fitted together smoothly, and there were no puckered places in the seam. After the parts of the moccasin had been sewn together on the wrong side, the moccasin was turned right side out, so that the seam would not show. If all the work had been done just right, a moccasin fitted smoothly, and was firm, but not tight. About eight pairs of moccasins could be made from one deerskin.

All the clothing of the Plains Indians was also made from soft-tanned skins. Men wore moccasins, shirts, high leggings, breechclouts, and belts. Women wore dresses, leggings, and belts. The children dressed like the grownups. Nobody wore any regular underclothes, but in cold weather the Indians sometimes put on two or three shirts or dresses at once, in order to keep warm.

The men's leggings and breechclouts together took the place of trousers. A breechclout was just a long strip of soft hide, drawn between the man's legs, and fastened under his belt. Strips or flaps of the skin were left hanging over the belt in front and back, like narrow aprons.

A man's leggings were also fastened to his belt. They were tied at the sides with strips of hide. The leggings were fitted close to the man's legs. If the leggings had been loose, they would have caught on things and been in the way when the man walked or rode. If the leggings were made to be worn for ceremonies, or other times when the man wanted to dress up, they had long fringes down the side seams on the outsides of the legs. It usually took a whole deer hide to make each leg of a pair of plain leggings. Another whole hide was needed to make the fringes on the decorated leggings.

It took at least four deer hides to make a man's shirt. One skin was used for the front and one for the back. Each sleeve was made out of a separate skin. The men's shirts fitted loosely, and were worn outside the belts, like sport shirts.

The women's leggings were shorter than the men's. They came up only to the wearer's knees, so one hide would usually make a pair of woman's leggings. These leggings were not made with fringes, since the women's dresses were long and the leggings did not show much.

It took six deer hides to make a woman's dress. There were two skins in the skirt; two in the blouse; and two in the sleeves. Sometimes the skirt and blouse were sewn or

MEN'S WEAR

BEADED SHIRT
LEATHER &
HUMAN HAIR
FRINGES

DEER
HIDE

THIS IS A
DRESS-UP
SHIRT

SIOUX
ABT. 1890

MOCCASIN

FUR LINED

BEADED
MOCCASIN,
CHEYENNE

CLOTH
BREECHCLOUT
BEADED TRIM
ON SOFT HIDE BELT

LEATHER
FRINGES,
BRASS
BUTTONS,
PIPE
BEADS,
PAINTED
STRIPES

KIOWA LEGGING
DEER SKIN,
MADE ABT. 1870

WOMEN'S WEAR

HIDE BELT

MODERN DRESS, BUCKSKIN
BEADED YOKE; FRINGE
MADE ABT. 1890 (SIOUX)

(KIOWA)
OLD STYLE BUCKSKIN
DRESS, HEAVILY FRINGED
MADE BEFORE 1870

SEPARATE LEGGING
& MOCCASIN. BEAD-
WORK ON COWSKIN.
(CHEYENNE)

BEADED
AWL & SINEW CASES
WITH SILVER TRIMMED
BELT PENDANT, BEAD-
ED KNIFE SHEATH
← KIOWA →

BUCKSKIN
LEGGING AND
MOCCASIN COMB-
INED. BEADWORK,
BRASS BUTTONS

tied together, but sometimes the dress was made in two pieces. A woman wore her belt outside her dress. On the right side of her belt, where she could reach it easily, she wore her knife, and on the left side were her sewing tools; her awl, and sinew thread, and cut-out work, each in a separate small case.

When a Plains Indian woman needed a new teepee, she saved hides for a long time to make it. To make a teepee for her family, the woman needed at least thirty-two big buffalo hides. If the woman were in a hurry to get her new home finished, she might ask her neighbors to trade her some hides that they had tanned. Then she gave her friends meat, or small deer skins, or helped them out with their work, in exchange.

After all of her buffalo hides were soft-tanned and ready to be sewn, the woman who was making the teepee invited her friends to come and help her work on the cover. The women made a sewing party of this work. Every woman brought her own sewing materials, and the woman who was going to live in the new teepee cooked a big feast for everybody. Usually one woman, who was especially good at doing such work, cut out the hides that were to be used for the teepee cover. The cutter gave each of the other women a share of the sewing, and told each worker how to fit the pieces together. All the women sat in a group, and sewed and talked, and at the end of the day the teepee cover was finished.

The poles for the teepees were cut in the high mountains on the western edge of the plains. The poles were usually made of cedar wood, because that wood dried evenly and lasted for a long time. The teepee poles were about twenty feet tall, and about twelve inches around. All of the branches and bark were stripped off the trunk of the tree, and the wood was trimmed down until the whole pole was of an almost even thickness. The upper ends of the poles were tapered a little, so that they could be gathered together and tied in a bunch. Some tribes used twenty poles for the frame works of their teepees, some twenty-two, and some twenty-four.

When a woman wanted to set up her teepee, she tied three or four of the poles together, a few feet from the top. She set the poles on the ground in a triangle if there were three; or in a square if there were four of them. She spread the lower ends of the base poles wide apart, so there would be plenty of room inside the teepee. Then she leaned her other poles against the first ones, filling in the spaces between the base poles. Last of all, the woman tied the secondary poles to the base poles by winding her raw-

hide rope tightly around the whole bunch. After the
poles were bound together, the end of the rope was left
hanging down beside the teepee door. Then the poles
could be separated quickly, by taking hold of the rope
and unwinding it. The door was an open space that was
left between two of the poles on the east side of the teepee.

After all the poles were set up, the hide teepee cover
was put over them. Two small poles were used to raise the
cover into place. They were left tied to the cover, and
hung down beside the door, to be used in regulating the
opening at the top of the teepee, where the smoke from
the fire went out. The fire was lighted in a hole in the
middle of the teepee floor. The smoke flaps, or teepee
ears, could be moved about when the wind changed its
direction, so that the top of the teepee acted as its own

chimney. The Plains Indians never built big fires inside their teepees. In fact, they had a saying that meant, "White man builds a big fire, stands a long way off, and freezes to death. Indian builds a little fire, stands close to it, and keeps warm."

The Indians had their own fire-making tools when they first went onto the Plains. All of the early fire tools

they had were made of wood. To light a fire in those days, an Indian man first laid a piece of hard wood, like hickory, pecan, or bois d'arc, flat on the ground. Then he set an upright stick of the same hard wood on the flat board. He took a small bow, with a sinew cord string, and fastened the bow string loosely around the upright stick. Then the man pulled the ends of the bow back and forth, making the upright stick revolve against the flat one.

The friction of the rubbing finally heated the board

until it began to smoke and glow. At the first sign of smoke, the man put finely powdered cedar or cottonwood bark against the end of the sharp stick, so the bark would catch fire from the heat of the friction. After the bark, too, was glowing, the man dumped it on small shavings, or dry leaves, or bigger pieces of bark, so that these things would catch fire. The last stage of fire-making by friction was to take the little fire that had been started, and put it against the wood of the main cooking fire. Making fire in this way was slow work, and it was tiring for the man who did it.

Later, after about 1850, when the white traders and soldiers brought them pieces of metal, the Plains Indians learned to strike the metal against pieces of stone, so that sparks would pop out. This is the same way that cigarette lighters work. Instead of catching the sparks on cotton wicks, though, the Indians caught them on bark or leaves. After the first sparks caught, the fire was lighted as if it had been started by rubbing. Still later, about 1880, when the white people began bringing them, the Indians were able to get matches, and to use them to make fires.

There was very little furniture inside a Plains Indian teepee. There were no chairs or tables; no stools or lamps or small pieces of furniture. The only pieces of furniture that the Plains Indians had were their beds. During the day time, most Indians used their beds as sofas, and sat on them. The beds were set up against the teepee wall, so that the center of the floor, around the fire, could be kept clear.

A Plains Indian bed was set up by putting four forked poles in the ground for the corner posts. Then four other poles were laid across the forks of the uprights, to make a frame. An extra pole was pounded into the ground outside the framework at the head of the bed, and another one at the foot. Slatted mats made of willow rods stitched together with sinew, were fastened to these extra poles. The mats were painted with horizontal stripes of bright colors, and sometimes were ornamented with deerskin tassels. The mats covered the bed frame, and served as springs for the bed.

Hides, tanned with the hair on, were laid over the bed

mats. The skins were soft and springy, and they made a warm, comfortable bed. The sheets on these beds were clean, soft-tanned deerskins. All the bedding used by a Plains Indian family was cleaned and aired and shaken daily.

When the family moved camp, the woman of the household took the beds to pieces and tied the poles of each bed together in a bundle. Then she rolled the mats around the poles, and wrapped the bedding around the mats. In this way she made a light, compact bundle of each bed. One horse could carry five or six rolls tied on a pack saddle.

The Plains Indian men made bowls and ladles to be used for cooking and eating. Sometimes the bowls were made of gourds, and the ladles almost always were. Sometimes the bowls were made of burls, or knots, that grew on the roots and trunks of trees. When a man wanted to make a gourd ladle, he took a ripe gourd, and cut it down on one side, so it would be the right size and shape. Then he scraped out the seeds that grew inside the gourd, washed and dried it, and the ladle or bowl was ready to use.

Making a wooden bowl was harder. The man cut a burl from a tree in winter, when the sap was out of the wood. The Plains Indians liked elm or cottonwood burls best, but sometimes they used oak burls. After the man had cut a burl, he hollowed it out by putting live coals on the wood, and letting them burn into it. When the bowl was deep enough, the worker scraped out the charred wood, and shaped the whole inside of the bowl with his knife. After that, he rubbed the inside of the bowl with fine sand, to make it smooth and clean.

Wooden ladles were made in about the same way as the wooden bowls. The men used the small burls that grew on the branches of the tree to make the ladles. They left part of the branch on the burl, to be used as a handle. After a wooden bowl or a ladle had been used for a while, it became smooth and polished, just from handling. Many old bowls, which are kept in our museums, are very beautiful.

Stone hammers were important tools in a Plains Indian household. The women used the hammers to pound up meat and fruit, and to drive teepee stakes into the ground. The men used the hammers when they staked out their horses; or when they pounded bark to use in starting fires; or for weapons in fighting. The men were the ones who made all the hammers.

To make a hammer, a man looked for a stone that was already smooth and rounded from time and wear. The best place to find this kind of stone was in the bed of a creek or river. After the man had found the right sort of stone, he made a groove around it, in the middle. He did this by pulling a wet rawhide string, dipped in sand, back and forth, back and forth, across the stone. The grooving took a long time. When the groove was finished, the stone was ready to be used as a hammer head.

For the handle of the hammer, the man used a piece of hard wood, like bois d'arc or hackberry, with a natural fork in it. The man fitted the grooved stone into the fork of the stick, and tied it there with a wet rawhide cord. As the rawhide dried, it tightened the two pieces of the hammer together. Sometimes a man made a rawhide cover that fitted over the whole hammer, including the handle.

In the days before the white people came to the plains, the Indians there made all their knives, and the points of their spears and arrows, of stone. The men had to hunt for just the right kinds of stone for these tools, too.

Flint was a good kind of stone for making knives and points, and many times the Plains Indians used it. Some white people today call all Indian points "flint arrowheads," because it is an easy name to remember. But just as often as they used flint, the Indians made points out of quartz or jasper. Sometimes they used semiprecious stones like agate or opal. In the northern plains, where there are large beds of volcanic glass, or obsidian, the Indians used that kind of stone. It all depended on where the worker lived, and what kind of stone he could find easily.

When he made a stone point or blade, an Indian man held the rough piece of stone flat against the palm of his left hand. He wore a strip of rawhide tied around the palm of each hand, as a protection. His tool was a piece of deer antler, held in his right hand. The man pressed the antler point down against the stone, with his whole weight. The weight, or pressure, of his right hand against the stone would break off small flakes of stone, one at a time, so this kind of work is called "pressure flaking." Sometimes a piece of stone did not break in the way that the worker expected it to, and had to be thrown away.

Then the man started over again with another piece of stone.

The Indians never made points by heating the stones and dropping water on them. They knew that most stones, if they are treated in this way, will explode. Then the pieces of stone fly out in all directions, and can cut or even blind someone who is near by.

After the Plains Indian man had made a point, he was ready to fit it to an arrow or a spear. The arrow points had to be made exactly right, so they would balance in the air when they were shot. Spear points did not have to be made so carefully, because the man used his spear for thrusting, and not so much for throwing.

A spear handle was usually made of a round limb from a bois d'arc, hickory, or hackberry tree. The limb was shaped with a stone knife and then was smoothed with fine sand. When the handle was finished, it was about three inches around and four feet long. Then it was ready for the point to be attached.

The man who was making the spear split one end of the handle in two, very carefully, and fitted his stone point into the cut. Then he tied the wood tightly around the point with wet sinew cord. If he wanted them, the man sewed rawhide grips around the spear handle with sinew thread, and the spear was finished. Sometimes the men decorated the handles of their spears with paint and feathers, but often they left the handles plain.

The men used the same woods in making arrow shafts that they used for spear handles. The shafts were shaped and smoothed in the same way that the handles were, but the workers were usually just a little more particular, so the arrows would balance and fly well. Usually the Plains Indian hunters used arrow shafts that were twenty-four to thirty inches long, so the weapons would be easy to use on horseback. Most white men, who shoot on foot, have longer arrow shafts.

The hardest part of making an arrow was the feathering, or fletching. The Plains Indians preferred to use the wing feathers of hawks or eagles for this, but some men used crow or owl feathers. The main thing was to have a feather that was long and straight and strong, and could be fitted to the arrow shaft.

In most of the plains tribes, the old men, who had plenty of time and patience for doing such particular work, were the arrow makers. Since they were often too old to do much hunting themselves, they traded their fine arrows to the other men for meat and hides.

When a man made an arrow, and had the shaft shaped just the way he wanted it, he fitted the feathers on. First he split a feather in half the long way, so its quill, or backbone, could be laid flat against the arrow shaft. He made three vanes, or split feathers, for each shaft. Then he tied the vanes to the shaft with wet sinew string, binding it tightly around the ends of the quills, but leaving the center part, where the feathers branched out, unbound. The combination of tying and gluing, when the sinew dried, was enough to hold the whole quill tightly.

Last of all, the point of the arrow was bound into a cut in the end of the shaft, just as the spear points were tied in. Then the arrow was ready for painting. Every man painted his arrows in his own way. Then, by looking at the painted designs, the men could tell who had shot which animal in the big hunts.

Like the spear and arrows, bows had to be made of hard woods. The Plains Indians preferred bois d'arc, whose French name means "wood of the bow," but they sometimes made their bows out of hickory or hackberry wood. Most Plains Indian men carried three or four lengths of bois d'arc with them at all times, so the wood could season well before it was used. Freshly cut bois d'arc is light lemon yellow in color, but it darkens as it seasons, and an old piece is almost the color of mahogany. If a bois d'arc bow had been carefully made from a piece of well-seasoned wood, it would last a man all his life. Some bows that are over a hundred years old can still be used.

The wood for the bow stave had to be cut in the winter, when the sap was down in the roots of the tree. The best wood was that between the heart of the trunk and the bark, where the wood was hardest and had the fewest knots. After the wood had been thoroughly seasoned, it was worked down smooth and narrow, with a stone knife.

The Plains Indians used bow staves that were about four feet long. This is shorter than the staves that white men use, because a long bow is hard to handle when a man is on horseback. The bow staves were slightly curved, so that the ends flared out and the middle drew in. The ends of the bows were notched to hold the bow cords. The curve in the middle of the stave made a grip for the archer's hand and a brace for the arrow. Sometimes the curve was bound with rawhide, to give the archer a better grip.

A Plains Indian man was always very careful of his bow. He always loosened the bowstring before he put the bow away, so the stave would not be pulled out of shape or lose its spring. He kept the bow stave, with three or four extra braided sinew cords for strings, in a watertight

QUIVER & BOW CASE
BUFFALO SKIN, BEADWORK ON
PATCHES OF CLOTH
(CHEYENNE)

rawhide case. He kept his arrows in another, shorter case, which was also waterproof.

In the Plains tribes, pipes were made and used only by the men. Most people know that the Indians invented smoking, and that white people did not know about tobacco until after America was discovered. Often people speak of "Indian peace pipes," as if those were the only pipes the Indians had. They do not stop to think that peace pipes were used in ceremonies, and that there were different kinds of Indian pipes for everyday use.

The kind of pipe that the Plains Indian men used most often was just a straight tube, like a cigarette holder. Often the tubes were made of hollow pieces of bone, usually of deer leg bones. When a man smoked this kind of pipe, he stuffed his tobacco into the end of the tube, and lighted it. Sometimes museum people call these pipes "cloud blowers," because they had to be pointed straight up at the clouds, to draw well.

In the evenings, when a group of men was sitting together and talking, they often used another kind of pipe. This was the stone pipe that people usually mean when they speak of a peace pipe. Instead of being straight, the stem of this pipe was bent like an elbow; and sometimes now we call them "elbow pipes." An extra long wooden stem was added to the stone stem of the pipe, to cool the smoke. The wooden stems were often very beautifully decorated with paint, quills, or beadwork. Not every man owned one of these fine pipes, so it was the custom for each man in the group to take a turn smoking the pipe.

The Plains Indians used a special kind of stone for making their pipes. This stone, which is dull red mottled with white spots, is called catlinite, after the first

CLOUD BLOWER PIPE
SMOKED POINTING SKYWARD
MADE FROM DEER LEG BONE
WRAPPED WITH SINEW
(CHEYENNE)

HORSE EFFIGY PIPE
BOWL OF CARVED CATLINITE
WOODEN STEM INLAID WITH
LEAD & DECORATED WITH
QUILL WORK & HORSEHAIR
(POSSIBLY SIOUX)

white man to describe it. The stone is found in only one place in the world: a quarry in North Dakota.

When catlinite is first dug up out of the earth, it is very soft and can be cut and shaped like clay. The stone hardens as it dries. After catlinite has been out in the air for a few days, it hardens and has to be worked like sandstone or limestone. The Indians who lived near the catlinite quarry made a practise of digging out the stone, which they called pipestone, and of trading it to other tribes. Because the Indians in the northern plains lived near the catlinite quarry, they had many stone pipes. The tribes in the southern plains, who were farther away, had very few of them.

Because the stone was not easy to get, stone pipes were treasured in most of the Plains tribes. They were used on special occasions, and were handed down from father to son.

In some tribes there were even stone pipes that were believed to be magical. Most of these belonged to the Indian doctors. Other magical pipes belonged to peace chiefs, or to Sun Dance chiefs, and were used in ceremonies.

Since the Plains Indians considered it an honor to be allowed to smoke a stone pipe, the custom arose among them of smoking one when a treaty was signed, or any kind of solemn agreement was made. It was like our custom of kissing the Bible, when a man takes office, or swears that he is telling the truth about something important. This is the custom that people mean when they talk about the Indians smoking a peace pipe. However, the Indians sometimes smoked the same pipes when they made peace and at other times.

In the very earliest days, right after the Plains Indians got their horses, most of the things that the Indians made were undecorated. But as the people traveled about the country, they found beds, or deposits, of brightly colored earths in the new places they visited. Someone had the idea of using the earths as paints, and so the Indians discovered the use of colors.

The earth colors were soft and pale, and we would think that many of them were dull. To people who had no other colors, though, the earths must have appeared brighter and gayer than they do to us. The earth colors that the Plains Indians used were mostly browns, yellows, and reds. Later on, the Indians learned to use berry juices or grape juice for blues, and to mix the juices with yellow earths, to make greens.

After an Indian man had dug up some of the colored

earths, he pounded them with his stone hammer until they were finely powdered. Then he sifted the powder through his fingers, and took out any coarse pieces that had been left in it. He tied each color in a separate buckskin bag, so it would not get mixed up with his other paints. He used the colors for painting anything he wanted to decorate; his weapons, or clothes, or even his face.

When a Plains Indian artist wanted to paint a design on a buffalo hide, he mixed his earth paints with water, putting each color in a small wooden bowl. Then he put a piece of sinew into the bowl with the paint, and left it there for the water to soften. This was like adding glue to his paint. It made the colors stick to the surface of the hide. They would not rub off on his fingers or clothes, if they were stuck down with glue.

The artist used a piece of porous buffalo rib bone as a brush. He put one end of the bone into his paint mixture, and sucked on the other end until the paint had been drawn up into the bone. Then he rubbed the bone over the part of the hide that he wanted to paint. Naturally, he had to have a separate brush for each color he used.

Before he started painting, the Plains Indian artist outlined his design. For this part of the work he used a small piece of bone, pointed like a pencil. He dipped the point of the bone in water, and then pressed it down on the surface of the hide. This made a fine groove in the skin, without leaving any colored line on it. If the artist decided he wanted a colored outline to show, he added it after the rest of the design had been painted in.

There was one thing that was especially interesting about the designs that the Plains Indians used. The men drew pictures of people, animals, and plants. They used these lifelike pictures in decorating the things that they themselves owned and used.

The Plains Indian women, on the other hand, used what our artists call "abstract" designs; that is, figures that are not meant to look like or to suggest the forms of living things. Usually, the designs that the Plains Indian women used were squares, triangles, straight or curved lines, or combinations of these geometric figures.

In time, each artist and each tribe came to like certain designs better than others, and to draw them especially well. This is what our artists call "developing a style." The style development in the plains went on for so long, and grew to be so strong, that people who have studied Plains Indian art can tell, by looking at it, by what tribe a certain piece of painting was made. Sometimes these

Painting a Hide

A Girl's Painted Wrap

people can even tell what artist did a certain painting.

In the northern part of the plains, many of the Indian tribes used porcupine quills to trim their clothes, bags, pipe stems, and horse equipment. The Dakota, or Sioux, tribes were especially skillful in this art.

Porcupines are slow, rather stupid, animals. The Indians did not have to chase the porcupines, or even to hunt much to find them, for porcupines live in trees and eat the bark from the branches. So when a Plains Indian woman needed a porcupine for quills, she sent her husband out to get one from the nearest grove of trees.

When the man found the porcupine, he killed it by

hitting it on the head, so the skin was not broken or the quills damaged. Then he took the porcupine home to his wife. She pulled the quills out of the porcupine skin very carefully, one at a time. The quills were loose, and would come out easily. As she pulled the quills, the woman sorted them. She put each size in a different buckskin bag.

Before she used the quills, the woman soaked them in warm water. Then she took each quill and pulled it flat between her front teeth, so it looked like a small ribbon. Then the woman cut off the hard, sharp, outer tip of the quill, and the quill was ready to sew onto whatever she wanted to decorate. The quills were stitched in place with sinew thread.

If the woman wanted to use her quills to trim a rounded surface, like a pipestem, or the grip of a bow or spear, she could braid them together into long cords. Then she wrapped the cords around the surfaces of the things she wanted to make beautiful. If the braiding and wrapping were done right, the woman could make a design with the quills.

Porcupine quills could be colored by boiling them with earth paints or berries. This took a long time, especially if the quills had to be boiled with hot stones. Many

QUILL PLAITING

SPOON HANDLE WRAPPED
WITH PLAITED QUILLS

QUILL EMBROIDERY
STITCHED WITH SINEW

workers liked the natural black and white stripes of the undyed quills, and did not try to change their colors.

After the white traders came onto the plains in the 1850's, they brought the Indians colored glass beads that had been made overseas, in France and Italy and Czechoslovakia. The Indians had never seen or heard of glass beads before that time, and they were delighted with the new way of trimming their clothing and moccasins. In a very short time the Indians all over the Plains began using beads to make the same kinds of designs that they had been making with paints and quills. Beadwork soon became such a popular craft among the Plains Indians that many people today speak of "Indian beadwork," as if no other people had ever made any.

In every Plains Indian tribe, though, there were always a few people who kept on using earth paints and porcupine quills. So it happens that when the last war came and the glass beads could not be imported, the Indians still knew how to make their useful things look beautiful.

10

WHAT THE PLAINS INDIANS ARE DOING NOW

Nowadays, when you go into the Great Plains, you see a farming country that is so rich and famous that sometimes it is called "the Bread-Basket of the World." The land still rolls and ripples like an ocean, but as time goes on the surface of the plains is becoming smoother. That is because men plow the earth and work with it. They, like wind and water, wear away the soil and change the form of the earth.

Where the two great buffalo herds grazed in times past, cattle are grazing now. Where the wild grass once grew "knee high to a man on a horse," wheat and oats and rye now grow as richly. The country that was open to the sky-line is fenced in, now, and the roads make straight lines across it. No man may ride across the plains as he pleases today; the roads are there to show him where he may go without doing any damage to the crops, and the land is fenced in to hold him to the lines of the roads.

Every farm on the plains has its house and barn and chicken coops, and at first sight all the farms look alike. If you come closer, though, you may see a house with a brush shelter built in the back yard. You may even find, in a pasture near the house, that a teepee is still standing. Then you know that you have found a Plains Indian home. The Indians still live out of doors in their brush shelters during the summers, and some of the very oldest people like to live in teepees all the year round. There they can sit and remember the buffalo days.

And, if you go into the plains country in summer, you may read in one of the newspapers that are printed there, or hear announced over the radio, the news that an Indian celebration is to be given. If you want to go to the celebration, you must drive over the straight paved roads for a long way. Then you turn off onto a dirt side road that leads back through a cow pasture, to a creek. There, hidden away from people who are not willing to take the trouble to hunt for it, you may see a Sun Dance given. But you will see that the dance and the Indians, like the country, have changed in some ways.

For instead of a circle of buffalo-hide teepees, you will

find a circle of canvas tents, or of trailers. There will be only a few horses tied near the Sun Dance camp, now, though many cars will be parked there. Nowadays, the dance usually lasts only two or three days, instead of eight, and very few men even hope that they will be lucky enough to see visions in the dance. Still the men dance, believing that it is right for them to thank the Power that made the earth for the good things upon it.

Nobody eats buffalo or deer meat, or wild fruits and roots in an Indian camp now. Instead, the people eat beefsteak, and bread from the grocery store, and canned fruits, and the children drink milk. The Plains Indians do not go hunting for food any more. Instead they work, like everybody else, to earn the money with which they buy their food. They do not receive any more help or money from the government than other farmers in the plains country do.

They are good farmers, the Plains Indians, and good stock raisers. Sometimes an Indian boy raises the best calf in his county, and once one of them raised the best calf in his state. Indian girls have won the contests in cooking and canning and dressmaking at state and county fairs. In some states the Indian children go to school with

The Old and the New

the white children, while in others they go to their own special schools.

Besides keeping up their dances and some parts of their old religious beliefs, the Plains Indians have kept some other things that they had in the old days. Most of them, even the younger people, still speak their own tribal languages as well as English. The Indians still remember the songs of the old days, and sing them at home when they are working or resting. Every Plains Indian has an Indian name as well as an English one. Every child knows the history of his tribe, as his grandfather has told it to him, and he is proud of the people who made the tribal history, and proud that he belongs to them.

Most of all, the Plains Indian men are still soldiers. They fought well and hard in the last war. Many of them were paratroopers, and asked to be allowed to fight with the sky troops because that was the most dangerous place to be. Some Indians were fighter pilots, and there were many Plains Indians who were military police, just as the members of the soldier societies were the camp police in the old days. The Army Signal Corps used a Plains Indian language as a code in sending messages. All the specially trained radio operators who used the code were members of one Plains tribe.

Some of the Indian soldiers were killed in the war, and their families mourned for them as if they had been killed on raids in the old days. Many more of the Indian soldiers came home when the fighting was finished, and their families held victory dances and give-aways for them, just as Plains Indians had always done. There were Indian girls who were WACS or WAVES or Army or Navy nurses, and their people were as proud of the girls as they were of the men who went away to fight.

The best thing to say would be that these first Americans are trying hard, now, to be like other Americans. The things that they are keeping from their old way of life are the things that any people would be proud of, and would try to keep. We know how proud they must be, for one of the surest signs that a white man is great in the plains is for him to be adopted into an Indian tribe. No white man who deserves it ever takes that honor lightly.

So, in spite of the changes that time has brought about, the Plains Indians are still the Plains Indians. They are not to be confused with any other Indians, or with any other people in the world.

ACKNOWLEDGMENTS

FOR MATERIAL USED IN PREPARATION OF

ILLUSTRATIONS

The American Museum of Natural History, New York City.

The Chicago Museum of Natural History, Chicago, Illinois.

The Denver Art Museum, Denver, Colorado.

F. H. Douglas, Denver, Colorado.

The Museum of New Mexico, Santa Fe, New Mexico.

The Oklahoma Historical Society, Oklahoma City, Oklahoma.

The United States National Museum (Smithsonian Institution), Washington, D.C.

Miss Amelia Elizabeth White, Santa Fe, New Mexico.

BIBLIOGRAPHY FOR ILLUSTRATIONS

Catlin, G. *North American Indians.* Eighth edition.

Denver Art Museum. Material Culture Notes Series.

D'Harnoncourt, R., and F. H. Douglas. *Indian Art of the United States.*

Dorsey, G. A. *The Cheyenne.*

Ewers, J. C. *Plains Indian Painting.*

Hodge, F. W. *Handbook of American Indians North of Mexico.* Report of the Bureau of American Ethnology, No. 30.

Holling, H. C. *The Book of Indians.*

Lowie, Robert H. *The Crow Indians.*

Lyford, C. A. *Quill and Beadwork of the Western Sioux.*

McKenny, J., and Wm. Hall. *Indians of North America.*

Mallory, G. *Indian Sign Language.* Report of the Bureau of American Ethnology, No. 1.

Marriott, A. *The Ten Grandmothers.*

Mooney, Jas. *The Kiowa Calendar System.* Report of the Bureau of American Ethnology, No. 17, Pt. 1.

Salomon, J. H. *The Book of Indian Crafts and Indian Lore.*

U.S. Department of Agriculture, Forest Service. *Handbook of Range Plants.*

Von Wied, Prince Maximillian. *Early Western Travels.*

Wissler, C. *The American Indian.* First edition.

Wissler, C. *Indian Costumes of the United States.*

Wissler, C. *Indians of the Plains.*